LIVING WITH GHOSTS
was first published in 2003.
It has appeared in Large Print editions
Chivers (UK) and Thorndike (USA) in 2004.

Critical acclaim for Paul Gater's other work:

'Brilliant yet subtle'
- The Times (*Biddy & Perry*)

'A beautiful book – it has everything'
- Les Scott, BBC Radio Stoke *(Astral Sex)*

'Fascinating, even addictive reading'
- Colin Clarke, MusicWeb International *(Summer with Bax)*

LIVING
WITH GHOSTS
An Investigation

Paul Gater

Anecdotes Publishing

ISBN: 9781898670 148
Text copyright © Paul Gater 2003, 2009

First published by Anecdotes, 2003
Large Print Editions published by Chivers Press, 2004 (UK)
& Thorndike Press, 2004 (USA)

Published by: Anecdotes
70 The Punch Bowl, Manchester Road,
Buxton, Derbyshire SK17 6TB
Printed and bound by:
RPM Print & Design, 2-3 Spur Road,
Quarry Lane, Chichester PO19 8PR

.

For further information go to
www.anecdotespublishing.com

Contents

To Dilys

Author picture by
Mark Campbell

Author's Note

When I first wrote this book I had no idea how successful it would be. Always having been fascinated by the supernatural world, I had often discussed the subject with friends, having experienced a number of inexplicable 'happenings' myself, which included several chance encounters with ghosts. Many people I met had had similar experiences, whether as one brief encounter or on a regular basis. These included psychics, those incredibly gifted people who actually 'go in' to help those already in the spirit world. In fact, several have since become friends of Dilys, my wife (who is an international psychic and writer) and myself.

Following publication, I was interviewed on five radio stations and by Sky TV. Indeed, one of my most vivid recollections was being interviewed over the phone by the presenter Shane O' Connor on BBC WM, just after midnight - the 'Witching Hour'! The book sold widely and went into public libraries, as well as going into Large Print editions both here in the UK (Chivers Books) and in the USA (Thorndike Press). I was also asked to regularly contribute columns to two local newspapers.

In the original introduction, I said that I was not writing as an expert but as a fascinated wanderer into the realm of ghosts. Inevitably, one learns. I found that many ghosts tend to manifest themselves on stairs and, during subsequent research, discovered that stairways represent a vital connection between our own 'earth' world and that of the spiritual. I was also unaware of any known ghosts which might have been recently active that were pre-Roman. Again, I was to find that the spirit of a Bronze Age horseman was encountered a number of times during the 1920s by several people at Bottlebrush Down in Dorset. The phantom horseman was seen and identified as such by a local archaeologist.

More people actually see ghosts than is realised, though there are those whose only 'supernatural' encounter is by way of the media. Inevitably the entertainment industry tends to 'hype it all up', treating the subject with sheer dramatic exaggeration. Even in traditional pantomimes, there are usually sketches for the comics which involve ghosts, whether the panto is *Mother Goose, Jack and the Beanstalk* or *Cinderella*.

Popular ghost walks around many of our towns and cities are often well attended and very informative. Some guides, however, tend to conduct them as jokey affairs – and it is true that some ghosts may be mischievous and jokey, just as they were perhaps when they were alive physically as people. But more often than not, phantoms which linger are of a more serious nature, 'stuck' here and unable for various reasons to 'pass to the light'.

But for whatever reason, the ghostly population (animal as well as human) seem to have left its spectral footprints across the vast domain of our many civilisations, past and present - in fact, across our entire history. So I have great pleasure in once again inviting readers to come with me on a journey to discover what it is like to be 'living with ghosts'.

Paul Gater

Introduction

Have you ever seen a ghost? Have you ever lived with one? A lot more people encounter ghosts or spirits than is generally realised, like those of former occupants of a house 'sitting at the fireside' who loved the place, or of persons from a time when a previous structure was built on the site. Ghosts are often seen and not recognised as such. Those dressed in old-fashioned clothing are obviously more likely to be. On the other hand without a spooky setting, how about the young man or woman perhaps seen standing in the lane who 'died' there in a motor accident as recently as two years ago? Some people may claim they have never encountered a single ghost, whether they believe in them or not. Whilst others – like myself - are very aware that they have seen ghosts and depending on their degree of awareness or sensitivity, some may even feel that they have indeed attracted such spirits to themselves almost throughout their lives.

I had always understood that a presence in a house might be happy, mischievous, troublesome or even downright malevolent. But there can also be more than one presence. Presences of all sorts and for all sorts of reasons other than just for the love of a place.

It could be for what would appear to us as a trivial reason like a place being altered; or perhaps the cause is something darker when either victim or perpetrator becomes 'stuck' at the scene of a crime; or the sufferer of a tragic accident, or a spirit needing to convey information to the person they were close to, still remains here on Earth. Occasionally a lingering spirit may be considered too evil to pass on. Conversely it could be harmless enough but just plain 'stuck' for no apparent reason.

Some of the examples of haunted dwellings I have quoted in the following chapters are from the Midlands area where I live. Others range from other parts of the British Isles and even other parts of the world. But hauntings, no matter where they may be are all the same, taking in the whole emotional range of the people they represent when they were here physically, whether the suffering of slaves or women in childbirth, grief, trauma, loss, terror – even love and joy – to whatever degree.

Every village and town seems to have and is proud of, its own connections with the spirit world. Several cities in fact have ghost walks as an integral part of their local tourist industries. Chester and York are perhaps two of the most well known while Derby, according to Sinclair McKay of *The Daily Telegraph,* claims to be Britain's most haunted city. Its total of almost 160 ghosts, so it is claimed, is 30 more than its closest rival York. But creating league tables as such using ghosts or entities I think is demeaning, as is the use of people in similar tables.

I have interviewed many people in the preparation of this book and what I found was an amazing diversity of stories on offer – from those who were taken aback by their one single experience of the paranormal to others who had encountered the phenomenon in its various forms many times, almost regarding it as normal.

I am not writing as an expert but as a fascinated wanderer into the realms of ghosts. However, as I wanted to get expert comment I approached people who have had specific experience of working in this field. One such is Jan Jordan, a clairvoyant, and resident astrologer for a newspaper which covers the Staffordshire-Derbyshire Moorlands. I spoke to Jan on several occasions and was fascinated to hear of her wide experience as a psychic over many years. Other experts I have consulted are Doug and Hilary Pickford who work as a husband-and-wife team using dowsing and mediumship – Doug is also a lecturer, broadcaster and author of many excellent books on Earth Mysteries.

Geraldine Edmonds is a working medium who lives in the South of England and is a fount of intriguing experience, as I discovered during conversations I had with her over the phone.

Brenda Diskin, a psychic and healer, is also from the south of England but is now living in Sheffield, South Yorkshire. She told me of two particularly sinister cases she has had to deal with.

Tim Chilton is the owner of what the media have called 'the most haunted house in England'. Although not a psychic himself he generously made me very welcome and provided me with much information during the visits I paid to the very atmospheric property during the early stages of my investigation.

I am gratefully indebted to all these people for their help and for their contributions to this book. And also to the following who, while very willing to share their experiences and expertise with me, did not wish to be identified personally. Consequently, I have used the pseudonyms listed below.

'Delia', a widely travelled medium has worked throughout the world; 'Fabia' is a psychic consultant and healer whose particular quiet directness impressed me very much; 'Mel and Amy Howlett', another husband-and-wife team, use dowsing and mediumship. 'Mel' in particular was very generous in spending evenings in discussion with me, especially when I was beginning my research, and providing me with a great deal of background information as well as stories from his own personal files.

I would like to say a particular thank you to my two 'resident experts' who were there throughout for discussion

11

and support - my wife Dilys, who is second-sighted and author of many successful books about her work as a psychic counsellor; and Simon Tansley, tarot consultant and psychic investigator. These two also agreed to participate in the question and answer sessions I include at the end of some chapters as throwing light on whatever aspects of ghosts and hauntings emerge in the previous pages. In fact these discussions could have taken up several books on their own! I found them amazing, intriguing and thought provoking, especially as my two 'experts' didn't always agree.

So it was well primed with much expert advice and information that I set out to tackle a wider public. And I found that everywhere I went there were 'ordinary' people eager to tell me about their experiences with ghosts. Without their tales and interest too, this book could not have been written. Again some people were happy to allow their names to be used, others preferred anonymity, but to all of them I am once again gratefully indebted.

The idea of encountering a phantom may not be a pleasant one. That is the primitive beast in us urging caution and because we do not feel in control of the situation. But such experiences can challenge us, help us to gain that control, understanding and where possible, ability to help a phantom or spirit, if need be, to go on its way.

So come with us on our journey from haunted inglenooks to the wider beyond we visited and share the excitement of what we experienced there!

Paul Gater

1

A Very Haunted House

Lowes Cottage is a grey sandstone three-storeyed early 19th century property in the village of Upper Mayfield, near to Ashbourne on the southerly edge of the Derbyshire Peak District. One's first impression is of a highly desirable country residence. It was built by a local stonemason, William Frith, and following his death in 1839 the house was sold and resold many times over the years and was also rented out. Complete with beams, a vaulted ceiling, an old range and other original fittings, it seems ideally situated 'far from the madding crowd'.

But for Andrew and Josephine Smith, a couple in their mid-thirties who bought the cottage in Hollow Lane in 1994, there was a different story, which I read absolutely fascinated, as detailed in the present owner's large scrapbook of press-cuttings. Graphic accounts were given of what the Smiths claimed had happened to them at the cottage.

Within twelve months of moving in with their young family, they reported, life had become a crowded nightmare of horrific smells, strange mists that moved from room to room, walls that would ooze with water, weird noises and an unseen ghostly presence. This seemed to attach itself to Josie, sometimes pinning her to the bed at night with considerable force, trying to smother her. On one occasion, she said, it even attempted to strangle her.

The Smiths had purchased Lowes Cottage for £44,000 from two local sisters Susan Melbourne and Sandra Podmore, who had inherited the property from their late father. Having raised only £41,000 from the bank, it was agreed that the shortfall of £3,000 be paid by instalments within three years. For Andrew, a joiner and Josie, a theatre nurse - both of whom had had financial problems but were now solvent – and for their children Lindsey, 8 and Stephen, 2 (another boy Daniel, was born two years later) the future seemed to be shining brightly indeed.

That was until the manifestations started, also according to their accounts the appearance of apparitions, sudden drops in temperature and periods when the strange mist was so thick according to Andrew that "you could lean on it". Although the unseen presence seemed intent on Josie, their daughter Lindsey claimed to have experienced nightmares and to have seen the figure of a young girl.

Was it significant that the cottage was built near to an ancient burial mound called in these parts a 'lowe', as well as the site of a gallows tree, and a Methodist Chapel? All these significant sites, in their different ways, might have provided a focus for otherworldly activity. And the history of the cottage itself hinted at potentially sinister events. For instance when the gallows tree, with its macabre association with captured soldiers of Bonnie Prince Charlie's retreating army from Derby in 1745, was felled, it was allegedly cut up and burnt in the garden.

There were tales still circulating in the village of how a young milkmaid Elaine Harring, who had lived at Lowes Cottage around 1861, had been incarcerated in the cellar, raped and murdered there. The Smiths discovered by searching through old records that at about the same time

Joseph Phillips, a young cowhand at Lowes Farm, had also lived in the house. It was said he had hanged himself from the rafters over the stairwell of the top floor – the perpetrator overwhelmed by guilt, perhaps? But frustratingly, nothing that could be found in any records confirmed anything untoward had actually happened to either of the young people.

A search of old records had been suggested to Andrew and Josie by the Reverend Peter Mockford, authorised by the Bishop of Lichfield to conduct ministry in the area of the paranormal and demonic. He had been called in by them originally to bless the cottage, but since this had not apparently worked, he thought research into past occupants might be a way of identifying the spirits themselves.

Rumours continued to persist. The Smiths heard of gruesome scenes wherein Elaine and Joseph had *both* been murdered. Their bodies had been buried somewhere in the grounds, it was claimed. So Andrew started to dig up the garden – even the cellar as well. But again nothing was found.

The Reverend Peter Mockford, together with his colleagues, is called out to many such cases every year. Most of them turn out to have no supernatural connotations whatsoever, but he told Ann Treneman of *The Times* that he believed Lowes Cottage was genuinely haunted. He had experienced the smell himself.

"Like rotting bodies. It was truly foul," he said. "If it was there all the time, you could say it was a dead cat under the floorboards. But it was not localised, and it moved around." He and his colleagues visited Lowes Cottage five times. Five times it was blessed.

The ghostly presence then went missing but events took a desperate turn when after four months, it returned. Now at their wits' end the Smiths were finally driven out. Leaving the keys with the bank, they fled.

In 1999, sisters Susan Melbourne and Sandra Podmore sued for their £3000. The Smiths counter-sued for £41,000, claiming they were not told the property was haunted at the time of purchase. The sisters said that it was never haunted in the first place. They had spent their childhood at the cottage, and nothing malevolent had ever been encountered. The Smiths, representing themselves, related their experiences to the County Court in Derby and were told by the judge, Peter Stretton QC, that he was reminded of Jay Anson's terrifying book *The Amityville Horror* which they admitted having read, but vehemently denied inventing the story of smells, creaking floorboards, poltergeists, oozing walls, deep groans, mists and sudden drops in temperature.

The judge however, remained unimpressed by the Smiths' witnesses, who included the Reverend Mockford, and evidence offered by two local ghost-hunters concerning the mist phenomena as well as a male voice they claimed to have heard via equipment they had set up in the cottage. Describing Andrew and Josie Smith as "hysterical" and "devious", His Honour ordered them to pay the outstanding £3000 to the original owners and dismissed the case. He said that if children had lived and played in the property and many other people had visited it and experienced no harm, then any threat of ghosts could not have existed. He dismissed also in his final summing up, stories of 'supernatural phenomena' "as more likely to have been created by man than by ghosts."

Soon afterwards the property was put up for auction. The event was featured in all national daily papers and on television. Who would want to buy, let alone live in, the most haunted house in England? The new owner was Tim Chilton, a businessman in his late forties. Amazingly he had been completely unaware of the property's reputation despite the media attention, until after the purchase. And as he told me later, he holds quite different views about ghostly intervention regarding Lowes Cottage.

All houses both old and new can be haunted – from an ancient farmhouse covered in ivy and hidden by trees, to that exclusive detached property on a recently-completed upper income bracket estate, or even the ordinary, modest semi-detached. Jan Jordan from Nottingham has travelled widely in the course of her work as a psychic and confirms this from her own experience.

"Owners or occupiers can sometimes be responsible for ghostly presences in the form of close relatives, spirit guides or something less pleasant," she says. "Or the spirits or ghosts may even follow a person from one property to another."

All the other people I have interviewed who work in this field agree with her.

Old hotels and inns are particularly prone to hauntings, having seen so many comings and goings, a constant ebb and flow of good and bad feeling over the years. And I found that there are arguably different kinds of hauntings. There are spirits or entities that are seen either once-in-a-while or regularly at particular times, like a video replay. There may be powerful feelings of oppression, phenomena such as fluctuation in room temperatures, water oozing from walls for no apparent reason or even poltergeist activity. And when we talk of 'presences', many may be from comparatively recent times as opposed to those of knights in clanking armour or headless Tudor types.

Some people move into a haunted house; some (as Jan points out) can take a ghost or spirit with them. There are haunted houses everywhere, people can live with a presence – sometimes more than one – whether they are aware of them or not. When I started to work on this book I was staggered by the number of people who seemed to turn up, some complete strangers but all with stories they were anxious to tell me.

I spoke to one old gentleman who recalled the time he shared a house with his younger brother and sister when they were students. His brother and sister were terrified by the figure of an aggressive-looking man trashing their kitchen one evening after they had locked up and they rushed into the other room to get him to help them throw out the intruder. When they all ventured back into the kitchen however, it was deserted. Yet the door and window were still bolted on the inside.

"All I could see was the state of the place!" the old gentleman recalled, shaking his head.

During their stay in the house his brother and sister regularly heard crashings and footsteps on the stairs and landing outside their bedrooms at night, while he saw and heard nothing.

"Thinking about it now," he said wistfully, "I've often wondered if I lacked their intelligence – was a duffer, or something."

Not at all. Indeed, I understand that some people are highly attuned to such things whereas others might not be attuned at all. Although most of us do seem to be, to a greater or lesser degree.

When I met Tim Chilton of Lowes Cottage, I asked him if he'd had any previous connections with ghosts either in regard to properties he might have lived in or on a more personal level.

"If by ghosts you mean things I see, no" he replied. "If you are referring to coincidences, events, odd occurrences – I've experienced a lot. But nothing visual."

"So since moving into Lowes you haven't actually seen anything?" I ventured, pushing for details.

"No, never."

What an anti-climax I thought, after all the stories, the media hype, the world wide attention the property had had lavished on it. But of course as we all know, ghosts tend to stick to rules of their own, they are not performers of 'party tricks' on demand. They may react in much subtler ways. In fact, I found it reassuring that Tim was inclined to be objective about his experiences. It made what he had to say seem more valid – to me at any rate.

"Have you sensed a presence?" I asked.

"A presence makes it sound like a localised thing," Tim replied. "I sense the place feels special, though it has changed since I came to live here, over a year ago."

I knew that clairvoyants and dowsers had visited the site and when I enquired whether they had picked up anything of interest he said they had all arrived at pretty much the same conclusions. The cottage is apparently situated on a convergence of various energy lines – some of which are referred to as 'ley lines' - against the next field in which there is an ancient burial mound – a 'lowe'.

Certainly a source of power more real than 'impressive' Hollywood green slime!

For evidence suggests that our ancestors had a keen knowledge of these lines of energy. It is even thought that they performed rituals to maintain their effectiveness, regarding soil fertility for the growth of crops, and their effect on the weather. Sources of water, such as springs and wells, stone circles, old burial mounds and places of pagan worship seem to have been linked by such lines of energy – mysterious and very powerful.

By now I was very eager to ask Tim if he'd been apprehensive about spending his first night in Lowes Cottage.

"It was really an almost classic 'night in a haunted house'," he replied firmly.

I listened, agog!

"Syon, my dog, can settle anywhere," Tim started. "With no furniture except for a blow-up bed, we were virtually as one, on the same level. He pricked up his ears, stood up as though really seeing something around. Strange for Syon, but in a manner which was in keeping with everything I'd feared. I remember thinking: 'I'm spending a night in Britain's most haunted house, with the dog going freaky'! For months I felt concerned. I would not go into a room without the light on, but it was actually very hard to stay there for that first night on my own when the media had been hyping it up so much – pages and pages of it."

I was not surprised. Brave man! In fact, I wondered if I would have kept my head under the circumstances. But there was more!

"The worst night was not actually the first but one a few weeks later," he resumed. "There was an absolute wind-up of a thunderstorm. Blue light and flashes through the latticework windows. It knocked out the electricity and it switched it on again. This kept repeating itself – on and off, on and off. It was like a Hammer horror movie, a horror-comic and I genuinely thought that night that I had bought a house I was not going to be able to live in. Nothing like it has happened since. It was the only time I felt 'I can't live here,' and it was so bad I even contemplated spending the rest of the night in the shed."

I put it to him. "Looking back now, what do you think was *really* happening that night?"

"It now feels like something of a turning point," Tim replied. "A breaking-point."

"A kind of test?" I suggested.

"Well thinking back, yes." he affirmed. "If I had not survived that night I wouldn't have been able to stay."

I asked him if he had experienced any manifestations of the sort other people had described, like the smell and the patches of damp on the walls.

"I can't vouch for the former. I have no sense of smell," was the reply. "Things to do with electricity seem to be the most obvious happenings. Things did switch themselves on and off. And I did experience the inexplicable patches of damp on some of the walls, including internal walls – though whether this was something natural or supernatural, I don't know. But it doesn't seem to happen now."

One of the things that still intrigued me was the atmosphere at the bottom of the cellar steps, which seemed to have been mentioned in all stories of the house in connection with the 'murder'. The dastardly deed was actually supposed to have been performed here, according to the old tales. This indeed is reputedly the most haunted spot in the whole building. So had Tim experienced anything in the cellar?

"The steps were the nastiest part of the house," he confirmed. "And I would avoid going down there at night. On the night of the thunderstorm, my circuit-breakers were down there! I have to admit, I kept well away!"

From such a rational man I thought this was a significant comment indeed.

Further points were clarified during my interview with Tim regarding the history of Lowes Cottage. During the 19th century, it was connected with not just one but a number of tragic young deaths, since at one period it had served as lodgings for apprentice stonemasons and people passing through the area. So as with any such dwelling there would surely have been a build up of emotion over the years.

But while Tim was showing me around I found I was mulling over the story of the gallows tree. Perhaps for me this was the most difficult tale of all to swallow. With the steep stone steps up the side of the cottage from Hollow Lane to the garden at the back, it seemed highly impractical that anyone would have dragged a large tree for burning up there.

Believing that the gallows tree had probably been felled some time in the 19th century, I was surprised to learn from Tim that the event happened only sixty years ago and that it was actually burned on a piece of common land on the opposite side of the lane to Lowes Cottage, where a new property has since been built. My instinct had been right – so much for at least one ancient tradition!

*

When Dilys and I were invited to Lowes Cottage and visited the village of Upper Mayfield, I felt there was a unique atmosphere in the house. It seemed densely charged, although this varied in different parts of the building – mainly it could be felt on the stairs and landing and the steps down to the cellar. I also felt that the cottage was eyeing us, like an entity 'taking stock' but cannot say it was any more than that.

I asked Dilys to give an independent assessment and report. Here is what she came up with:

'I might not feel the 'atmosphere' of a place immediately. It can take time. But my impression of the village as a whole was that it was a secretive sort of place; indrawn.

'In the garden of Lowes Cottage I did pick up a strong energy force in the ground. There was probably water deep down. I had this sense that the garden was more the focus of natural energy than the house. I thought it might have been part of an old burial ground or a place of sacrifice going back to some ancient religion. Something significant could well be found in the earth, but not particularly a body of someone comparatively recently murdered.

'In the cottage itself I felt a distinct sense of repression, particularly in both stair wells. At the bottom of the cellar steps, there is very much a

22

presence of past people. I 'saw' a young girl, aged about fourteen or fifteen, with dark hair that was short or else was pulled back. She was wearing some sort of long dress, with laced-in bodice and cut-away neck, with something like a pale kerchief or smock underneath it.

'But the strongest presence there was that of a man in his late twenties/early thirties, wearing a cloak or coat with a high collar. A person maybe who stopped over at the house on his way to somewhere. I picked up the place name of Manchester. Some sort of commercial traveller possibly, from the 1800's.

'Between him and the girl I picked up no real relationship as such, but he might well have been a repressed type, the sort of man who molested young girls in dark corners, then pretended it hadn't happened. So regarding the supposed rape, in my view it was more likely to have been a sexual assault of a lesser degree. The girl, young, inexperienced, might not have known the difference. More likely she panicked, became hysterical and accusing. I didn't feel that she played any major part in the story of the cottage.

'Another man whose presence I sensed was more recent. Again there was sexual repression, but this time puritanical and over-reactionary. But regarding a repressive atmosphere, if anyone were to pick up on it with hang-ups of their own then these might well be encouraged, or even activated. They could pick it up and become victim to it.

'I think women were passive victims over the years in this cottage, which was mainly male dominated. As for the supposed stories of murder I don't think there is any indication of anything tragic between the young girl and the young cowherd. No murder but perhaps some kind of unfortunate accident.'

A further more general comment of Dilys's is I think relevant here: *'Often the darker spirits are in need of help. They have already suffered in life. The dark and shadow sometimes has to be there; it cannot be moved on. It may hurt you to deal with it, but hopefully you will have compassion on them all. One who victimised in life was*

23

victimised at some point himself. Cruelty is an expression of extreme fear, weakness, hurt and pain.'

In view of the report of Andrew and Josie Smith and his own experiences – as well as the fact that quite a few people had also commented on the area around the cellar steps - I wondered what Tim Chilton thought of Dilys's comments.

"I can't complement or endorse what Dilys has said, because I haven't got past the point that I just didn't like the atmosphere in the cellar. Except again that recently it has changed. I have been working down there quite a bit, seeing to the doorframe, door and so on. It now feels increasingly nice and cosy, like the rest of the house, and I'm fascinated by that."

"You think the atmosphere in the cottage is completely different now to how it was when you bought it?" I suggested.

Tim agreed with this, adding "Now the cottage feels far more restful."

He explained that he had always felt the cottage was a very positive place for him, and that if any ghosts were there they were good ones.

"Because of your attitude?" I asked.

He was reluctant to commit himself.

"I can't say that, exactly," he answered. "Having met Andrew and Josie Smith several times, from what they told me of their experiences here they came over as pukka and thinking individuals and I was convinced they were telling the truth. They'd had their tensions, and I think they were genuinely scared out of their wits. And I think a building can capture that. A place of power, if you like, to use negatively or positively. So while I find that this cottage suits me more than I could have dreamt, it actually frightened them away. A strange, strange place!"

What the experts say

Paul: Simon, from the psychic investigator's point of view, do you think it is significant that Lowes Cottage is built on a convergence of lines of energy and that there seems to be some connection with the burial mound in the adjoining field?

Simon: Yes, certainly. Dilys mentions in her report the feeling she had in the garden, though I haven't been there myself so can't comment personally. But if it's an old house, there are probably connections to ley lines, maybe an ancient site there, an old well, therefore an ancient spring, so that would inevitably attract spirits because of all the energy. Even if a spirit is still here on this planet, it is looking for ways to move on and it gets attracted to certain places.

Paul: Would you say then that the house could be occupied by ghosts or spirits that were not actually there when they were physical, alive as human beings?

Simon: It sounds like a very powerful place, and as has already been mentioned energies are neither good nor bad. They just are. But that strength and power can, as Dilys suggests, attract a repressive force, which can attract more. There are different feels about different places.

Paul: Could such a force be eliminated, got rid of?

Simon: I think there are ways of working with it. I agree with Dilys in that there needs to be a balance of dark and light, but if it does become unbalanced, the balance can be brought back. More light can be brought in so things are evened out. Energy lines can be diverted, moved round the building. But all that happens then is that the energy *in* the building is dissipated. I use copper rods to divert certain energy lines, but not all. Others are just 'there' so a different kind of working is needed. There are so many different sorts of energy lines and some can be a problem.

Paul: So if a person of a happy and optimistic nature moved into such a house, would that help allay the repressive energies that might be present?

Simon: It might do. But ultimately you would have to confront the energies. Happiness can quite easily disappear and when negative things start to happen to us they can drain us. Some places are just like that.

Dilys: I once lived in such a place myself. It simply saps your energy to keep going - even to exist. In the end I thought 'I just can't stay here any longer.' I had to move out.

Simon: Some buildings are built in the wrong place that's all. And although there are exceptions, older buildings aren't usually as bad as the more modern ones, which may have been built without care anywhere. If an area of land has been left clear for a long time, then there is generally a reason. The old builders knew when it wasn't wise to build because of ley lines, or fairy paths, or whatever. Although this doesn't mean to say the place is a 'bad' place.

Dilys: It's not a suitable place, perhaps. Because of the energies.

Simon: In Chinese terms, they say never build near a burial ground, because burial grounds are yin and we, as human beings, are yang. Again it's a question of finding a balance. We can't take too much yin.

Dilys: It's like visiting a stone circle and feeling the energy present. Places of power. People never lived there. They lived elsewhere.

Simon: Such a place can feel very uplifting, and have a very positive effect but only if you spend short periods there. Long-term, it can be debilitating. That's why some people in houses built on ley lines can have ill-health. Their energies are being drained away.

2
A World Of Their Own

We as human beings and they as phantoms, ghosts or spirits –
call them what you will – do we both inhabit the same world,
albeit in different compartments perhaps? That is hard to say
but I prefer to think that we – and they – live in different
worlds, with that tantalising common ground between where
both worlds engage.

Theirs is different, appearing to least respect the so-called
physical logicality of our own. Hence spirits may 'illogically'
inhabit a hollow in the landscape where a house no longer
exists, or appear to walk through a wall where a gate or
doorway has long been blocked up. Nor are the processes by
which potential phantoms are elected (or elect themselves) for
their role very clear. Though some seem pretty obvious: if
two people were involved in a murder, say, only the spirit of
the victim is generally seen – according to European folk-lore,
displaying the wounds responsible for the demise of its
physical self.

It is easy to understand why spirits haunt certain places -
public buildings, for instance. These are settings to a plethora
of human activities. Theatres and sometimes cinemas are
almost always traditionally haunted, though on investigation I
found that it is not necessarily the large events or big names
that tend to linger. Rather it is those who held responsibility,
worked there or cared for the place with devotion who want
to hang about. I have spoken to several theatre personnel
about their experiences. Nearly all theatres are proud of their
ghosts and superstition is part of the actor's trade. Brian
Beech, formerly Technical Manager of the now-closed

Theatre Royal, Hanley told me that several people had seen someone in uniform walking round the building, like a *commissionaire*. Although he had not witnessed anything himself Brian had the feeling sometimes that while working, he was being closely scrutinised.

Graham F. Humphreys, now retired, has spent his life in theatres and cinemas. For many years he was a Relief Manager for the Rank Organisation, working at venues all over the country. He told me that on arrival he always made a point of walking round a venue when it was empty to really pick up the atmosphere.

"Buildings will talk to you," he says.

One of the places he worked at just previous to his retirement was the Coronet Cinema, Notting Hill Gate in London. Originally opened as a theatre in 1890, the building contains the original dressing room that Sarah Bernhardt would have used. And Pavlova also performed on the Coronet stage. Their ghosts have never been seen as such but Graham and others have felt the theatre had a particularly good atmosphere, in spite of it being said that a young woman had jumped off the front of the gallery because her boyfriend had been killed in the Boer War.

On one occasion late one evening, Graham's bunch of keys – the Manager's keys for the whole building - were dropped accidentally down the back of a sealed radiator.

"Instead of panicking," he recalled, "a great calm came over me. I felt as though some presence was giving me support. I've always taken the view that if a presence is there, it will recognise me as a friend. And without all the difficulties I expected, the keys managed to be retrieved and I was able to lock up for the night."

He says that every theatre and cinema has atmosphere. Not so perhaps when first opened, it tends to build up over time with packed houses, all sorts of people, rich and poor, everyone with something in common. These are places of leisure, friendship and happiness.

Spirits can follow people from one place to the next regardless of time and distance. Or they can remain tied to significant places such as their graves, or a hanging tree of execution - both of which provide a focus for high emotion that could still linger.

I was told of an elderly lady we will call 'Jane' who, while reminiscing about her courting days in the 1930s, witnessed such a ghostly happening. Sitting on a seat waiting for her young man in St Edward's churchyard in Leek, Staffordshire, she first noticed that something was wrong when all the birdsong started to fade. Then she heard singing and about twelve monks came through the gateway of the churchyard, carrying a bier. This was laid on the ground and they buried someone in a newly dug hole. A burial service was conducted in Latin and as they chanted and sang, the spectacle faded and gradually the birdsong returned, together with the noise of the traffic. Jane claimed this happened on two occasions.

When I investigated, I found this particular church had been under the auspices of the monks until the Dissolution of the Monasteries in the 1530s. So Jane seemed to have witnessed something that probably took place at over 500 years ago. The monks could have been from the Cistercian Dieulacres Abbey, the ruins of which are situated about a mile beyond Leek, near to the Macclesfield-Ashbourne Road. It was founded in 1214 by Richard of Poulton on an already holy site on extensive areas of land in Staffordshire owned by the great Earl of Chester, Ranulph de Blundeville.

When I read up about the abbey I found Ranulph a terrifying character, villainous and cruel, giving land to the Church to save his soul from his sins. History shows that ghosts can walk as a result of such ambivalence. Being a tyrant need not mean a person is not aware of the world of spirits. In fact, according to the Dieulacres Chronicle, this abbey was actually founded through ghostly intervention.

One night in 1206 Ranulph claimed to have had a dream. The ghost of his grandfather gave him the directive to take the monks of Poulton Abbey, near Chester away to the safer environs of Leek, in order to escape the raids that had been taking place in the area of Poulton-on-Dee by the marauding Welsh.

But as the saying goes, 'To dream of the dead is to be troubled by the living', and Ranulph was certainly under stress at this time – not only about Cistercian monks. Marital, family problems and matters of a political and religious nature were adding to his burdens. No doubt he had probably brought most of them on himself!

Great care was usually taken when someone died to help the spirit to depart from this world as easily as possible. In Scotland for instance, it was once thought that the spirit of the deceased might be unable to leave the immediate area of the grave because of the veil of tears shed by relatives and friends. Some cultures took active steps to ease the passing. The North American Indians, believing the spirit to exit through the top of the wigwam, would beat the sides in order to drive it on its way. Similarly, an old English superstition declared that all doors and windows of the house should be opened to help the spirit leave as smoothly as possible.

But I found that such superstitions often contradict each other. In some other parts of Europe it was believed that all doors and windows should be barred and bolted, and the body of the deceased was removed via a hole knocked through a wall. This was a clever strategy because the spirit had to leave through an exit point it would not normally have been aware of, which was then quickly filled in. So even if inclined to wander, the spirit would be unable to gain entry anywhere should it return. Sometimes the house of a deceased person, together with all personal belongings, was torched. Such ideas reflected a conviction that so far as possible, every link with the spirit's physical existence should be severed. The ghost would depart, having no reason to return.

But of course, come back they do and to all sorts of places – manor houses, cottages, old pubs, anywhere and everywhere that might have been primed atmospherically by the years of comings and goings of people, with their mix of profound emotions. And they bring their own particular stories, their own emotions with them.

At Michaelchurch Court in Herefordshire a ghostly woman is said to appear in the oldest part of the manor house, dating from the 16th century or earlier, whenever a female child is born into the family. Looking for her own baby, perhaps? Or was she less sentimentally a medieval feminist? One wonders whether her spirit still walks, the house having been unoccupied at least since the 1970s.

The large, three-storey, 19th century Gothic style school building in the village of Staunton-on-Wye, again in Herefordshire, is reputedly haunted by an elderly man who peers out through a top floor window. Bricks would be thrown down the chimneys in the middle of the night, strange noises were often heard, pet dogs would howl, and the school bell would ring seemingly of its own accord. When occupied by the Army no-one would sleep in the reputedly haunted room – which surely says something for the old man's energetic tenacity. But his ghost obviously thought its reign of terror was justified.

The restless spirit was that of George Jarvis, who died in 1793 aged 94 having made his fortune in the leather trade. In his will, £30,000 was to be put in trust for the benefit of the folk in his own village of Bredwardine and for those in nearby Letton and Staunton-on-Wye, for the provision of food, clothing and medicines. A stipulation in the will strictly forbade any monies to be appropriated for the erecting of public or private buildings.

George Jarvis's daughter Mary, who had been excluded from the will, contested but was overruled and as late as 1852, a Royal assent was granted whereby monies could be used to build schools and almshouses within the three parishes. And by the 1970s, the school building at Staunton-on-Wye was being used as a Youth Hostel.

So no wonder the eccentric benefactor, objecting to his money used for purposes of bricks and mortar, is still to be seen glaring angrily from that top-floor window. What *is* amazing is that the building where he makes his presence felt did not even exist during his lifetime!

The female phantoms at your fireside need not necessarily be the traditional vague 'white lady' or 'grey lady', spooky and undefined. Women in the past led perilous, earthly lives. They experienced the obligatory risk of numerous childbirths, they slaved long hours and worried about their families, they had all the same fears of mothers today about the safety of their babies and children. Women have always feared whatever has threatened, whether war, loss of their men-folk, rape and pillage, plague, sickness and death. More recent times have added to personal anxiety – the coming of old age, loneliness in some 'home from home', or even just a child or member of the family going into hospital.

'Men do the fighting, women do the worrying', as the saying goes. So it is no wonder so many women are still there in their familiar, accustomed place at the fireside. They linger even though their world has moved on.

Here, however, is where the quirky nature of spirit thinking makes itself apparent. Many properties today, old and new, do not have a fireside. They have central heating. The spirits can still be stuck though, and need help.

As Dilys pointed out:

"One has to think of ghosts or spirits as once having been people like us, probably with all sorts of hang-ups – a man who couldn't cope with his responsibilities in life or a woman who felt unloved and desperately needed a hug. As psychics working with ghosts, we do not usually encounter things like evil incarnate or demons. It is far more likely to be about helping lost or frightened souls on their way, very much like working in a war zone, dealing with the displaced. There are some psychics who actually work in what are called Spirit Rescue Circles.

"Many of the spirits one encounters are traumatised, in a state of shock at having died. And as a medium, I find that what seems to be crucial is the attitude they had towards life when they were alive. It's mostly the ones who saw no way forward in life who can't move on after death, and whether people believed there was anything after they died doesn't seem to have any bearing. Ghosts generally in my experience are very focused in on themselves – crying, upset, etc. Even if they seem to be focused on another person, the motive is probably more selfish. But if it was generally realised that spirits were ordinary people once with human strengths and weaknesses, I think it would make 'ghost stories' as such much less frightening and much more interesting."

Jan Jordan described a typical case involving such a frightened and stubborn spirit. Here in her own words is her story of what happened when she was called out to 'The Lilacs' in Alfreton, Derbyshire which proved to be a far from average semi-detached.

"The family were quite distressed. They had already had visits from the clergy and puzzled council officials. The house was fairly small with a lounge with open plan stairs, kitchen and two bedrooms. I saw a man, small, dressed in black, with a hat similar to what a Quaker would in the past have worn. He was sitting on the stairs then he went up toward the bedrooms, but I knew he was watching me from the top corner. The lady of the house told me that they were so upset they were sleeping downstairs. They were getting poltergeist activity upstairs – light bulbs popping, doors slamming and locking, noises, items being thrown around.

"We lit candles, then I went upstairs on my own and walked round. Sitting down on one of the beds, I felt a sudden thud at the side of me. A swirling, smoky light shot through the darkness across the room. I knew this entity was trying to threaten me. He certainly didn't like my presence. I had to let him see I was not afraid and that my powers were stronger than his. I told him he should not be here.

"I sat there half-an-hour quietly in the darkness with this 'friend', but was determined he had to go. I could feel him struggle with the situation, but after a while I sensed him leave. I then walked through the upstairs rooms and could feel the cleansing. What I noticed though with this family was that Mum and Dad slept in the front bedroom, and four girls from 11 to 17 years, plus a boy of 9, slept in the back bedroom where the thud on the bed I sat on had happened. Poltergeist activity was probably attracted by these children in the first place. A few weeks later the family were re-housed by the council."

Jan also told me the fascinating tale of her experiences at an old hostelry whose atmosphere had certainly been primed by the comings and goings of many generations. This was the Poste Chaise Hotel at Bishop Auckland, County Durham.

"I was working at a Psychic Fayre at the Hotel, which is situated in a prominent position facing the market place. It dates back a long way, but its Function Room and Restaurant were added on at a much later date.

"As you walk into Reception, you can see straight through the Restaurant area and into the Function Room. To the right of Reception is the old part, which is a lounge-type public bar, still old-fashioned with low, beamed ceilings, bench seats and open fire, with lots of brasses. As I stood waiting in Reception, looking down through to the Function Room, I could see a man in top-hat and cloak right at the far end, just still, looking towards me. A quick glimpse, then he'd gone.

"As I went into the Function Room, I was drawn towards the wall facing me. It seemed to be out of focus, moving. The longer I looked, the more it seemed to swirl until it 'opened', letting me see a dark, cobbled courtyard with carriages entering through a large archway at the back. Some sort of commotion was going on, and men shouting in the rain. And there was the man in top hat and cloak.

"Later I enquired about the building, asking the staff. When the Hotel was first built it was just a coaching inn. Where the Function Room is now, it used to be a courtyard, with an archway for carriages and horses. I had seen men in a fight, and I believe one was killed.

"My room upstairs also left me with a lasting impression. During the night I was woken up by a voice talking very close to my face. I also heard what I thought was rustling skirts. I saw a young woman – slim, dark hair, very pale, looked about 20. I was 'told' she had been brought here against her will. Her father had arranged a marriage for her that she didn't want. She had committed suicide. I wanted to help her, and said she could come home with me and I'd help her pass over into the light, into peace. But she said she had to stay: she was trapped here. I explained she should be able to go now, but I don't know whether she listened.

"Next morning I was told by the hotel staff there was a room with activity, and that none of the maids would enter it on their own. Number 22 – the one I was in. The staff also told me that a young woman had been seen many times on the stairs and landing, with skirts rustling. And in the

Function Room, the man in top hat and cloak had often appeared."

After attending a Psychic Fair at the same venue some time later, Jan was once more booked into a room for the night – but, alas, not number 22. Next morning a fellow clairvoyant who had stayed in that particular room did talk of an encounter with the spirit of a young woman during the night, with rustling skirts. The spirit had obviously decided not to move on – or couldn't – despite help having been offered.

During research undertaken for this book I came across many stories like this. The exploitation and victimisation of young women seems to have always been an accepted part of the fabric of society. Here are two more typically brutal and dramatic examples that illustrate this sad fact.

Brymbo Hall was a large part-Elizabethan dwelling near Wrexham, North Wales that was demolished in the 1970s, the whole area being developed for open-cast mining to supply coal to the Brymbo steelworks nearby. Prior to its demise, so it was said, the building was haunted. One story was told of the daughter of the household, another young woman who chose death as an alternative to entering a marriage arranged by her father.

During a ball to celebrate her twenty-first birthday, she suddenly rushed upstairs in tears, much to the surprise of the many assembled guests. Time passed and she had not returned to the celebrations. She was found in a small room, high up in the house, where she had hanged herself. And from that day the atmosphere at Brymbo Hall changed. Even when it was no longer occupied, the caretakers said that dogs would never enter that small room – the 'haunted room' as it became known – and that the windows would never stay closed, even if they were secured with string or wire. By the next morning, they would always be found wide open.

A woman who grew up locally recalled going with her neighbours into the cellars of the Hall, to escape the air raids during World War Two. When I asked her about the ghost she said:

"We had some strange experiences there. But no-one actually saw anything. More like presences, they were. Doors would open by themselves and a bitter cold wind would come rushing into the room. It seemed to get inside your mind. "

Apparently the spirit of the distraught girl still lingered. And a similar story was reported by the dowser Mel Howlett and his wife Amy when I interviewed them.

They were called to a small shop in a North Midlands town, where the owner told them that he and some of his customers had regularly seen a young woman move from the door, and walk through an interior wall, where there was a mirror.

"We both felt a strong presence when we got there," said Mel. "We were overwhelmed within a few minutes by an enormous feeling of distress, frustration, emptiness and loneliness. We made contact with the spirit near to some stairs.

" 'Come! Come!' she pleaded. 'Please! Can you come?'

"Using my dowsing rod, Amy and I followed the presence up the stairs into a room right over the shop. The feeling of despair up there was so great we were both stricken by it, so much so we were reduced to tears. All we could say was 'How can we help?'

"Amy, a gifted medium, then said that it was a young girl in childbirth alone.

" 'They've all gone away, locked the door,' she reported, caught up in the tragedy.

" 'She cannot get help, and she's screamed and she's cried. She dies in childbirth, because she haemorrhages. No-one came. It was a cry for help. A cry discharged into the building.'

"You see," Mel explained "when you get past the death experience, time and distance mean nothing. The echo of such a cry goes on and on. For those who are aware it remains there. Amy and I had walked right into it and we empathised deeply.

'We know! We know what happened – we're here' we said.

"The girl had been 'stuck' since sometime during the 19th century, and we told her that there were those who would help her now, wherever she was. We contacted the spirits to lead her on, and she realised that someone had actually listened. Although we were too late to save her in life, the feeling of isolation had been left behind. Amy and I went back the next day, the next and the next. By then the feeling had completely dissipated from the building."

What the experts say

Paul: Simon, talking about atmospheres, do you believe that a new public building – a theatre, cinema or concert venue say - has very little atmosphere when it's first opened?

Simon: It depends on what was there before.

Dilys: People don't generally realise there's no such thing as a completely 'new' and untouched site on land anywhere. Over the centuries there have been battles, old settlements, burial grounds, even just a place where one person felt something very keenly.

Simon: You do have to bear past history in mind. But generally I agree, new places don't have much atmosphere.

Paul: So you think we leave something behind in places over the years - that an atmosphere, whether of warmth or something else gradually builds?

Simon: Emotionally and psychically, we're shedding something of ourselves all the time. Like a slug-trail!

Dilys: No-one seems to have any choice about whether they're going to be a ghost or not though, or in what lingers and what doesn't. I mean, you often hear people threaten 'I'll haunt you!' but they generally don't. The choice is not ours.

Simon: No, though there are times when people do seem to stay or come back deliberately. Sometimes as you've said, Paul, there are people who stay somewhere because they loved the place so much.

Paul: Like the lady who appeared in the house whenever a female child was being born in the family? I suppose births are emotive, significant occurrences and many ghost stories do seem to be about warnings of things about to occur.

Simon: Yes, there's a wide tradition about warnings. In Ireland the banshees can turn up when something dire is going to happen, and black dogs are often supposedly seen as warnings of doom.

Dilys: You shouldn't try to invent motives for spirits. I'd like to have met the people who've actually seen this ghost of the woman who keeps appearing at female births because you know, stories like that can just have been passed down for ever, sometimes with no real foundation.

Paul: I believe as recently as the 1970s, an investigator spoke to the owner of Michaelchurch Court who claimed the ghost had appeared at her own birth, then subsequently at those of her two daughters. Any thoughts?

Dilys: My feeling about this one was that it might have been the spirit of a retainer, maybe an old nurse who always came to oversee the births. Probably not a frightening thing, more a person who wanted to help because she loved the family and always attended to the cradle, who was moved by something young and female in her charge.

Paul: What about the vision of the monks in the churchyard at Leek?

Simon: More like what I'd call a trace, a phenomenon that just repeats itself over and over, a bit like a looped tape.

Dilys: Although again, I would have liked more information about the incident. It could be that the woman picked up on something significant. Maybe the monks were burying someone who'd died in a plague, or particularly tragically. Or maybe the funeral was for a person especially revered, like an abbot. I would like to have asked Jane where it happened in relation to the church, because there might be something in the ground there that would shed light.

Simon: All kinds of people come back. There are dozens of kinds of energy. For all sorts of reasons. You get to know what is likely to happen if you work in this field.

Dilys: Yes, sometimes you might be wrong, but you do get a 'feel' because spirits seem to have their own rules. The famous ones for instance – Katheryn Howard running screaming at Hampton Court is almost certainly just a trace. You couldn't help her really. She isn't there, it's an echo, like a film projected on a screen. But in the cases you've mentioned in this chapter – the old nurse, and the old man worrying about the way his money's been spent - I think they're more active. Probably they feel responsible, as though nobody else would do the job properly maybe. They still feel they need to supervise things themselves. This is one of the things I mean about ghosts being self-centred.

Paul: I suppose Jan Jordan's experience when she witnessed a scene previous to the Function Room of the hotel being built – that was probably also a trace?

Simon: Yes.

Paul: But what about the many stories of the ghosts of women who died to escape arranged marriages or in childbirth? These were victims, surely. I mean, they were still suffering.

Dilys: Well, there are an awful lot of stories where young women have apparently died tragically – either in childbirth or trying to escape their fate in some way. I have to admit I find them a little suspicious. I've mentioned before that we must remember ghosts were people, not saintly innocents. And I think even though society was different then, the girls might not always have been helpless victims, they would at least in some cases have fought back, shown their spirit as they do now. Often we're inclined to view the case in rather a fictional manner and I personally have rarely come across the 'dying in childbirth/escaping an arranged marriage' scenario. There was one case where I identified the spirit of a girl crying hysterically in someone's flat. I thought: 'Ah, here's one of those dying-in-childbirth cases or someone who was badly done to'. But try as I would, I couldn't relate it to that sort of tragedy, the spirit was simply crying with temper because she couldn't get her own way. That moment was where she was trapped, and when I cleared things up for her – spoke to her sharply, as a matter of fact, as you would with any live teenager - she went quite peacefully on her way. Once again, evidence of being self-centred rather than some kind of cosmic victim.

Paul: Would you simply dismiss such stories then?

Dilys: Oh no, I am sure there are genuine and very terrible cases. The one described in this chapter – the one Mel and his wife dealt with – certainly sounds extremely sad and I have personal experience of heavily traumatic cases of similar suffering and cruelty, unfortunately. We know they exist. But one of the worst problems for an investigator is to avoid becoming too emotionally involved.

41

Simon: Your involvement will encourage you to make assumptions, like finding just a skeleton and then adding something to it.

Dilys: It's all terribly emotive. You must never be 'e-motivated' by what people say they have seen and heard. Or even what the ghosts themselves tell you often. In fact some ghosts – if you met them as people – you'd run a mile. You wouldn't want to be 'e-motivating' with them at all.

Simon: And ghosts can con you in lots of ways.

Dilys: That's absolutely true.

Simon: No ghost is going to say 'I was a bad guy.'

Dilys: Exactly. If a ghost was a habitual liar in real life, it will still be that. Some ghosts are their own best PR men.

Simon: The thing is this, we move on to other places, we get reborn and some of these spirits or ghosts who come through – perhaps representing themselves as parents, grandparents, or very sympathetic characters - aren't necessarily who they say they are. Parents and grandparents, for instance, may have been reborn and are back on this planet in other bodies, doing something different. What we're actually getting perhaps are some of their image traces – their physical impressions - that some other entity has taken over. Many entities have their own agendas, and they may be trying to get through back to this earth using whatever focus they can.

Dilys: Entities can be very manipulative. They could well be saying "Oh, I was left here. I was abandoned. I was tortured, tormented." And everyone would be saying "That's so sad! Let us help, etc!" and the 'thing' is probably sitting there enjoying itself no end.

Simon: "All these people are feeding me with energy!"

Dilys: Yes, that's right! And the more the entity says: "Help me more, help me more" the helpers could actually be assisting it to perpetuate itself.

Paul: It seems to me in fact, where ghosts are concerned, you have to avoid extremes in the way you react. It's just as potentially dangerous to be frightened by feeling they're terrifying monsters as it is to get drawn into their personal dilemmas.

Simon: Absolutely. You said earlier on that we inhabit different worlds. And however we might want to, we can't live in theirs.

3

Close Encounters of the Ghostly Kind

Amazingly, almost everyone has experienced some strange encounter or other, or knows of someone else who has, within that common ground where our world and the spirit world tend so frequently to merge. Typical, I suppose, are those experienced by Paul Delicata, 23, a trainee physiotherapist. I say 'typical', yet every encounter is interpreted differently through the perception of each individual even when two people or more witness the same thing, albeit together or individually and at different times.

There are some people who claim to have encountered ghosts or spirits for most of their lives whilst for others this has only started to happen comparatively recently, as though a gift of perceptive ability has remained dormant, to be awakened by a chance remark – even a trite one - or by some happening.

Like myself Paul has always been interested in tales of the supernatural, but he says that it was seeing the film *Sixth Sense* that first triggered his ability to 'pick up' things.

"The first time I ever saw anything," he informed me "was at Marie, my girl-friend's house. Marie and I were sitting up late talking and it was about midnight. I'd been to the bathroom where her mother had recently had a shower fitted, and as I came out, I turned to close the door after me, I saw that there was a small child standing in the shower, with no clothes on, with its arms crossed over itself. I got the impression it was looking directly at me and I felt so embarrassed. I thought it was Marie's younger sister and I said 'Oh! Sorry!' and went out quickly. But when I mentioned it to Marie, she checked her sister's bedroom and she was there fast asleep, as was everyone else who was in the house."

As far as Paul knows, the spirit, or trace, of the child has not been seen again. He also detailed a more recent occurrence.

"Marie and I – had been out with some friends for the evening and were on our way back home in the car. It was about 2am. We were sitting in the back while my friend, who was driving, was in the front with his girlfriend. Granted I was 'under the influence' but not much, and I could certainly tell what was reality and what wasn't. Well, looking diagonally through one of the front windows from the back of the car, I saw this 'thing' in the beam from the headlamps. I was able to follow it with my eyes and as we went past a junction in the road, I realised that 'it' – the 'thing' - was actually a 'them'!

'Did you see those two people?' I said. And everyone said 'No!'

"But where they were standing, in the fork of the two lanes, it would have been impossible not to have seen them. The second person had its back towards the car as we went passed. The first one I could see was dressed darkly, maybe with a cloak, with a sou'wester, or a tricorn hat on his head. It was weird. Perhaps they were waiting for a coach. People nearby in Bagnall village (Staffordshire) say that the ghost of the highwayman Dick Turpin has occasionally been seen in the area."

Paul's girlfriend, Marie, remembers being told of an encounter her grandfather, a reliable, no-nonsense type of countryman, had as a young man. He was cycling along a lane in Bagnall early one morning when he saw what he believed was the spirit of a young woman with long hair and what looked like a wedding-gown on. She appeared to float across the lane in front of him, then jump straight over the six feet high hedge on the opposite side. An athletic girl!

There are numerous examples of people 'walking in' unsuspecting on ghosts. Derek Dymond, who lived in a terraced house in Tunstall, Stoke-on-Trent told me how he came in late one November evening and before settling down to watch the Late Show on TV, went into the kitchen to make himself a cup of Ovaltine.

"When I came back into the living-room," he reported, "I suddenly saw this bloke sitting at the coffee-table. 'What are *you* doing here?' I shouted, thinking he was a burglar. 'Get the hell out of it!'

"He turned, looked at me," Derek continued, "and he disappeared. He never came back."

Asked to describe the intruder, he said that he appeared to be completely solid. He wore a collar and tie, was bald and had glasses, and was probably early middle-aged.

Derek mentioned the incident to a friend who, some time later, happened to get into casual conversation with an elderly man living just across the street from Derek. The talk was about the history of the neighbourhood and past occupants of various premises that the old gentleman could remember. No mention was made of any ghost, but it emerged that many years before, Derek's house had been occupied by a father and son who used to deliver coal. The son had always worn collar and tie, was bald, and had glasses!

Another series of encounters from the Stoke-on-Trent area was detailed to me by Ella, (not her real name) who had a ladies' hairdressing salon. Her tale is told in her own unmistakably racy style.

"There was always a smell of violets on the premises and I was constantly asking customers if they'd used violet scent. The answer was invariably no, but as I'd always sensed some sort of 'presence' around I put the aroma down to that. Anyway, I eventually saw 'my' ghost – and it wasn't what you might have expected. It was a little old man!"

Ella did not perhaps realise that there might have been two presences. Some mysterious lady possibly, had been responsible for the violet scent. I did not think Ella's ghost was likely to be wearing it from the way she described him.

"I was doing a customer's hair and I could see the entrance and hallway through the mirror. He was standing out there – very old, very decrepit, with an old-fashioned walking-stick and a little cap. I assumed he wanted to see my brother Jack, who had a jewellery business upstairs. But Jack was downstairs on my floor, in the kitchen having a coffee. So I went to the little old man and asked him what he wanted but he didn't speak.

"Well, I went and told my brother that someone wanted to see him, and he went to the door of the salon but the little old man wasn't there. So he went upstairs – the little old man wasn't there either. But there was always the smell of violets, which I found comforting.

"Mind you," she went on, "I felt sometimes it could've been the little old man who got up to pranks. One day, one of my assistants and me went upstairs and Jack was showing us five expensive rings he'd just bought. Next thing, I saw a hand come up from under the table and grab the rings and I thought it was my assistant.

" 'But Ella!' she protested, 'I haven't touched them. The rings are still there!'

"And so they were. Then my assistant suddenly let out a scream as she felt what she thought was something like a cigarette-end being stubbed against her leg. When she looked, there was a distinctive burn mark there!"

47

This only intensified my impression that the prankster definitely did not sound like someone associated with peacefulness and violets! And there was more.

"On Saturdays, my sister used to come and help out," Ella continued. "This one Saturday, about quarter-to-nine, she went upstairs to the toilet and just called: 'Hi, Jack!' to our brother. Then suddenly, she heard someone out of nowhere say a very loud 'Boo!' And my sister practically fell downstairs and said, 'Ella, I'll kill our Jack for frightening me!' She told me what had happened. I said 'Sorry, Sis, but Jack hasn't come in yet.'

"Well, from that day, she never went to the toilet again. She'd rather use the one down the street, by the bank."

But not all residential ghosts are as mischievous as this. I spoke to a lively, middle-aged couple from Swadlincote in Derbyshire, whom we'll call Trevor and Linda. They told me about the old man who sits on the stairs of their recently completed home, happily smoking a once-famous brand of cigarette. He feels he is welcome, very comfortable, and is looked upon as part of the family.

Trevor said that their friendly spirit had followed them when they had moved home several times over the years. When he described its appearance to his elderly mother, mentioning a specific item of clothing that it wore, she was immediately able to identify it as the spirit of his grandfather – who apparently had always smoked Woodbines, and had always worn a red, spotted bow-tie! Trevor had only vague, childhood recollections of him, but felt reassured that the old gentleman still held strong affection for him and for his family.

Psychic Jan Jordan experienced a resentful ghost when, after she and some friends had attended a Psychic Fayre in Birkenhead, they stayed at a guest-house on the outskirts of the area overnight. The owner was an elderly gentleman, very quiet, who kept to himself. Jan takes up the story:

"The place was a large semi-detached, in an avenue of similar houses. My bedroom was at the front, with a huge bay window. There were two single beds and bunk beds. I was tired after a day at the Fayre, our not having got back to the guest-house until gone midnight. I was waiting for the kettle to boil to make a much-needed night-cap and decided I would sleep in the bed nearest the window when suddenly a smoky figure of a woman walked into the room, passed me, and sat down on the bed I was planning on sleeping in. She just sat there, facing the bay window. I couldn't believe she was so strong. I knew she was telling me I wasn't welcome there. That was her room.

"I apologised and explained it was a guest-house now, and that I was there just the one night. She didn't seem to fade for ages. Anyway, I had my drink and decided to sleep in the other bed instead. I was woken up by a rippling sensation. I could feel the quilt being lifted up and sensed that someone was getting into my bed – although I had the light on and there was no-one there except me.

"I didn't sleep the rest of the night because I knew I wasn't alone and the next morning at breakfast, as our group all sat round the table, I told them what had happened. The proprietor smiled wryly, quietly went into the lounge and came back with a framed photograph of his late wife. She was the same woman I had seen in my bedroom."

There have been some occasions when I too have walked into the realms of ghosts and had close encounters with them, unsuspecting. In fact ghosts could not have been further from my mind each time. Once I was with an elderly relative as she was being transferred late one night from the Emergency Department of a hospital, to a ward to be prepared for surgery. As the two porters were pushing her along on the trolley – with me following - we suddenly seemed to leave behind the bright lights and hectic dashing about of a modern hospital.

Turning a corner at the end of a deserted corridor, we appeared to descend into a long, poorly-lit tunnel with, much to the patient's discomfort, a cobbled floor. The walls appeared to be of dark-coloured bricks. Although I said that I was not thinking about ghosts, perhaps it was because of my heightened state of mind that I was aware of several medical staff – nurses from the 19th century – quickly standing aside as we wended our way along the tunnel. I had the vague impression of large, starched headgear though I could not describe them further but I knew they were there, as though putting their heads together and making comments. I suppose I might have asked the porters whether they had seen or felt anything, but they were busy people and the thought simply didn't enter my head at the time. As we ascended a slight incline, it seemed we were soon back into the bright lights and noise of the 20th century.

Another encounter happened a few years ago in my job as a horticulturalist, when I took over the large, neglected garden of a house just south of the Staffordshire Potteries. After about a week I told the owner of the property, a fairly matter-of-fact businessman in his late fifties whom I'll call 'Ralph', that sometimes I'd thought someone had been watching me from the terrace, although I had not seen anyone actually up there. The only people usually in the house were Ralph's mother-in-law and a family friend who came in to help with the housework. But this seemed something very different.

"I'll say nothing," Ralph commented, rubbing his chin pensively. "But keep me informed."

The garden itself consisted of large areas of lawn, herbaceous borders, island beds of trees and shrubs and an extensive rockery. It fell away fairly steeply on all sides and took in commanding views of the surrounding countryside – even on clear days, the distant Welsh hills to the west. By the following week I had managed to grub out a lot of self-sown sycamores from among more choice trees and shrubs. One morning I remember feeling a few drops of rain on the back of my neck. I looked up for some reason – towards the terrace. And suddenly I saw him.

"A tall man. Elderly. Broadly-built," I told Ralph next time we spoke. "With a clipped white moustache. He had both hands in the pockets of a khaki-coloured slop. He also wore a cap. He was there one second, gone the next. He definitely seemed to be watching me."

Ralph smiled. With a sense of relief, I felt. Apparently I was the only other person apart from himself who had seen the figure. Whenever Ralph had mentioned it to his wife and their grown-up children they had been extremely dismissive about it.

The house and garden had been built in the 1930s for the previous owner, a prominent potter, still a household name. For the final twenty years of his life he had lived for the garden, never getting his hands soiled but supervising his small team of gardeners from the terrace. He had died at the house five years before I arrived.

During the following eighteen months, as restoration and replanting progressed I saw Mr X frequently, always watching with a keen sense of interest and instantly disappearing when I stared back at him. The atmosphere of both house and garden was very positive though, and I sensed that there had been a lot of happiness around.

It was by coincidence that I discovered the lady who was the immediate neighbour to Ralph had actually worked for Mr X some twenty-five years previously at his factory. It had been his custom, she told me, to open the garden to his employees for one Saturday afternoon each summer. Snapshots she showed me of one such occasion portrayed various people relaxing in areas that by now were very familiar to me. And on one? The boss himself, looking very affable, a tall, elderly man I recognised, quite broad in build, with a clipped, white moustache.

This did indeed seem a haunted place. Ralph told me that apart from being aware of Mr X around the garden, at about 7.30 some mornings while in the kitchen, he would also catch a fleeting glimpse of the spirit of *Mrs* X in a blue housecoat, coming down the stairs, crossing the large entrance-hall and disappearing into the lounge.

As a final comment, Ralph's elderly mother-in-law described to me how she had witnessed something else of interest.

"It was one night in summer," she began. "I'd woken up. Definitely woken up. So I wasn't dreaming it. But outside, I heard music. Sort of dance band music. I think it was being played on an old gramophone. I looked out of my bedroom window and there below, on the grass among the trees, were people dressed all smart, but colourfully. They were all talking and laughing. There was food and drink on a long table. I could tell they were having a good time – a party time. One or two were dancing to the music. And – yes – it was an old gramophone. Then suddenly, everything faded. All that was left was the grass, trees and the moonlight."

She experienced that vision only once, so far as I know, but in a way it endorsed my own feeling and that of others, that there had been a very happy, ongoing sense of energy about the place. The fact that Mr and Mrs X had done a lot of entertaining during their time there certainly added to the positive atmosphere.

Two or three years ago Marnie, the landlord of a public house in Newcastle-under-Lyme asked Dilys for a reading with the tarot cards. After the consultation, which had taken place in the empty Bar, Marnie remarked that she had always felt that there was a nasty presence behind the bar itself. But because Dilys was not asked for an opinion in this case, she did not pursue the matter. However what she did pick up in another part of the room was the spirit of a little old woman, shabbily dressed, with a dark shawl drawn about her.

Marnie said that a number of her customers had actually seen the woman, and that although she seemed to be standing inside she would in fact have been standing outside the pub, against a wall that had been demolished when the building had been altered. Originally this had been the site of a 'hole in the wall' where a person bringing his or her own jug could buy ale without entering the pub.

Concentrating on the original part of the room, Dilys saw it 'open up' on to a scene from possibly a century before – the floor made of earth, roughly eighteen inches below the present level. There were lots of men, very crowded in a smoky atmosphere. What light there was, Dilys thought, could have come from a fire. Amid the general feeling of bustle and *bonhomie* there was some sort of game being played on the floor, and small dogs were running around.

"They were probably playing bar skittles," Marnie told her, "and the dogs were probably whippets."

Dilys said she felt that the men had connections with the sea – or water, anyway – even though Newcastle-under-Lyme is nowhere near the sea. Marnie told her that they would have been bargees. The canal had passed close by and this particular establishment had once been a regular stopping-off point for the watermen.

It is interesting to point out that although the little old woman was present, she did not appear to participate in the scene just described and Dilys got the impression she was from a different era altogether.

Many ghosts or spirits appear out of their time and place – existing in that merging in the ether, as previously mentioned where times past and present become connected in some way, albeit in brief but repeated episodes. Or on the other hand, is some form of time travel involved? When something from the past is witnessed in the here and now, does that something visit the present or is it the witness who – however unsuspecting - enters the past?

I brought this up with a number of people - including some clairvoyants, but they said they could not decide, although Dilys did say that as she worked with the past, present and future, for her it was a matter not of time but of altered states of consciousness. Whilst picking up the scene from a century or so back in time at the pub for instance, she was well aware of 'being' in the past, but also knew that physically she was still in the present.

Past, present – so what of future indicative? Since before Biblical times dreams have often been of great significance where prediction is concerned.

"What's this to do with ghosts?" you may ask. Well, in dreams when we see images of ourselves, maybe those images are actually ghosts of the future, forewarning us of something whether good or bad. There are many recorded examples of this happening to famous people.

Spencer Perceval, the British Prime Minister who was shot in the lobby of the House of Commons on May 11th, 1812, foresaw in a dream the manner of his own death in some detail, including a description of his assassin. The event was also 'seen' by at least one other person – John Williams, a Cornishman - unknown and unrelated. So concerned was he about his prophetic dreams that he felt compelled to journey to London to warn the Prime Minister, but was dissuaded by his family. The crime, however, took place exactly as both of them had foreseen.

Abraham Lincoln foresaw in a vision in 1860, on the night of his election as President of the United States, that his destiny was to serve two terms in office but that he would die during the second. He predicted later (to Harriet Beecher Stowe, author of *Uncle Tom's Cabin*): "Whichever way the war ends, (the American Civil War) I have the impression I shall not last long after it is over."

In less than a week after the Southern surrender at Appomattox, he was assassinated, the tragedy a fulfilment of yet another dream Lincoln had confided to his close friend Ward Hill Lamon only a few months previously. He had seen, he said, the draped and shrouded body of 'The President' lying in state in the East Room of the White House, mourned by weeping crowds of people, 'killed by an assassin.'

Romula, wife of the great dancer Vaslav Nijinsky, dreamed she saw her mother being murdered while she sat in her dressing room, combing her long hair. Her mother, a famous Hungarian actress, was shot by a vindictive dresser who had been dismissed from the theatre, hours later, exactly as Romula had foreseen.

On a happier note Romula also 'saw' her meeting with Nijinsky, the fact that she would follow the Ballets Russe to England and the details of her own wedding in a church in Buenos Aires – a year before she so much as put eyes on her future husband.

According to certain legends the scene of a fatal accident or where murder has been committed may be haunted by the phenomenon referred to as the 'headless ghost', which has puzzled the student of folklore for generations because the victims were not necessarily decapitated in the first place.

Possibly there is something much deeper in origin than, say, Anne Boleyn walking the Bloody Tower 'with her head tucked underneath her arm' in the song made famous by the late Stanley Holloway (although of course, she *was* decapitated). All the same, many weird and wonderful tales involving heads or the lack of them have been the stuff of storytellers for a very long time.

For instance at Great Melton, where the old Norwich road once skirted a deep pool, its depth unknown at the time, it was said that at midnight and again at mid-day, a horse-drawn coach driven by a headless coachman, accompanied by headless footmen and carrying four headless women dressed in white would quietly rise from the water, move silently round the adjacent field then sink into the pool again. Many years before, members of a bridal party were being driven along the road. The coachman was drunk, there was an accident and everyone was drowned in the pool.

As a slight variation to the tale the story runs that those who see the girls' faces will have good luck. For those who see their headless torsos the omens are dark.

Possibly the ultimate headless ghost story concerned the unfortunate young Lord Dacre of Gilsland, in the North Tyne and Border neighbourhood. He was murdered in 1569, thanks to the machinations of his guardian Sir Richard Fulmerston, who had 'fixed' a favourite toy to cause tragedy. Ever since, the headless ghost of the child has been seen riding up and down on the instrument of his death - a wooden rocking-horse that is also headless!

The old belief is that if one is visited by a headless ghost then one's own demise is imminent. Every Saturday night in Doneraile, Ireland long ago, it was alleged that a headless coachman would drive furiously through the streets, stop outside different houses, and bang upon the door. If anyone was foolish enough to answer the knock, a container of blood would be thrown in his face - the inevitable would of course, occur within a very short time.

What the experts say

Paul: Simon, in cases where people have seen a ghost or trace just the once then it has disappeared, does that mean it has actually made just one appearance or might it be haunting the place for a longer period? The child in the shower, for example.

Simon: We can't know, but I get the feeling they're around more than just once.

Paul: Any comment about the case of the man appearing in the terraced house who was mistaken for a burglar?

Simon: You mentioned that when some people see a ghost it can seem like the awakening of a skill, the ability to perceive if you like. A lot of people see ghosts and don't realise it because they can be so seemingly real and so matter-of–fact. It's only when one is encountered in an unusual situation where it might not be expected that the reaction is 'Oh! That must have been a ghost!' I'm sure there are a lot of ghosts about – just wandering around the town, as it were. And people simply take them for granted as normal unless they're wearing unusual clothes. Even then they can be considered as on their way to a fancy-dress party or even plain eccentric.

Dilys: If you're a psychic or connected with this sort of work you do not feel you are seeing anything odd. You accept it. Those who only see a ghost once generally find the experience seems completely matter-of-fact and real to them, not 'spooky' at all. People don't appreciate how normal it is to be psychic, how natural to be able to wander in to these other dimensions.

Simon: But I think there are other considerations to be taken into account when ghosts appear. A change of atmosphere for example, when things go cold. When they see something some individuals can get more scared by the atmosphere, the cold, rather than by the sight of the actual spirit itself.

Dilys: Any spirit that is not of this dimension will need something from the living, some source of energy in order to manifest itself physically. It's not trying to frighten you usually, the cold feeling just happens. I experience this – the coldness - when I know spirits are around me and I just accept it as normal.

Simon: Someone less sensitive wouldn't perhaps pick up on the actual atmospheric change but simply pick up on the visual.

Paul: Yes, thinking about those 19th century nurses I encountered, I knew they were there, I felt them. I could 'see' them in my mind's eye even though I couldn't really have described them.

Dilys: You're dealing with an extra sense, you are talking about something that does not exist within the limitations of your five physical senses. Obviously there is no language you could use to describe the experience.

Paul: Simon, why can some people pick up on spirit, but miss out on something like atmospheric change?

Simon: I think we're all adept in different ways. Some people are clairvoyant – they 'see', others are clairaudient – they 'hear' and others clairsentient – they 'sense'.

Paul: I was thinking of those hospital porters, who'd probably been along that 'tunnel' many times, with patients in the course of their duties.

Dilys: People do not appreciate that many staff who work in hospitals, nurses especially, are perfectly well aware of other worlds, and the kind of spiritual experiences people have when they are dying are quite common. But they don't talk about it. They accept it.

Paul: Have you anything to say about prophetic dreams, ghosts of the future?

Dilys: When you are out of the physical dimension there is no time, there is no place, so time is irrelevant. You could be looking backwards or forwards. Most people can remember what happened in the past. But if you've got psychic sight where you see things in the future, you don't remember them, you're 'pre-membering' them. You're seeing them with as much vividness as if you're looking backwards. It's like saying something or other happened ten years ago. Well, you could look forwards with psychic sight and say something *will* happen in ten years from now with just as much certainty. So you're dealing in another dimension altogether.

Paul: Could you comment on 'headless ghosts', why they're associated with accident or crime, regardless of whether or not the victims were actually decapitated?

Simon: Ghost stories I knew in my childhood, the ghost nearly always had its head tucked underneath its arm! There are so many stories of headless ghosts that there must be some embroidery going on in them. Why haven't they got a head? What's it really about? A connection with scenes of accident or crime gives a possible direction to look into although I don't think that's the whole story.

Dilys: You could probably link somewhere along the line with ancient beliefs, pagan traditions. The pre-Christian Celts were head-hunters for instance. Believing in reincarnation, they cut off the heads of their enemies to prevent the spirit from re-occupying the body. Because they considered the 'life' was in the head, they – the Celts – would acquire the strength of their enemies in this way. There are all sorts of beliefs like that. Interestingly, in my work as a medium I find that departed spirits of people who might have had their heads cut off or have been blown to pieces or carbonised in this life, have been completely whole once they pass across.

"I'm here, I'm all in one piece!" was the message of a man I recently contacted. Thinking he simply meant "I'm here! I've arrived!" I didn't know at the time that he'd been horrifically attacked with an axe before he died. This only came to light when the woman who'd asked me to make contact with him actually told me some of the details later.

4
Haunted Grounds

'Haunted ground' does not necessarily mean it has to be populated by ghosts or spirits. Ground can also hold feeling, exude atmosphere. This need not be about one thing but is more likely to be of a collective nature: for example where things went on for a long time, such as activities at Bronze Age burial sites, plague pits, churchyards, castles, or dungeons, places that held a lot of fear, suspicion and secrecy. Where something like long term child abuse has occurred people can pick up that sense of deep unhappiness and feeling of hopelessness for centuries afterwards.

Similarly where murder, particularly multiple murder has been committed it is often impossible to clear a property of its terrible association, its feeling of high emotion and negativity. Drastic action is sometimes called for. The house in Gloucester belonging to Fred and Rosemary West, the setting for numerous horrific killings, was knocked down. Whether the ground it stood on was afterwards blessed, I do not know. My guess is that one of the more practical reasons for its demolition was to deter morbid curiosity.

Locations where animals have been killed can be sensed. Not only the sites of old abattoirs but farm buildings and land at the back of old farm cottages, where 'unofficial' slaughter used to take place. Along an old drovers' road for instance, the atmosphere may still be permeated by the animals' feelings because they would certainly have known they were being taken to slaughter.

A patch of land I knew well near to Newcastle-under-Lyme conveyed sadness and suffering, the atmosphere at times heavy and stultifying. Dilys sensed that there had been death and destruction there in the past. Maybe plague. She also 'saw' what seemed like smoke, burning debris and holes in the ground, reminiscent I thought of those old photographs from World War One, of fields and woods blown almost into oblivion. Then I suddenly remembered my parents telling me when I was about fourteen, that they had been informed the land was once a smallholding. Swine Fever struck some time in the 1920s and after being slaughtered, the pigs were burned here and their remains buried.

Larger areas too may be endowed with a feeling of negativity – the aftermath of plague or bloodshed from long ago or the attitude and deeds of some previous landowner. Negativity tends to breed further negativity, trapping people who come along in due course into like-mindedness.

This was exactly what I and a number of other people felt throughout the 1970s, when working at Trentham Gardens near to Stoke-on-Trent. The same feeling could be felt throughout the 700 acre estate, but more especially in the formal Italian Gardens overlooking the fine lake.

On several occasions in summer, when working in that area on my own in early morning before the arrival of tourists and other visitors I would sometimes pick up a strong feeling of despair. This seemed to embody itself in the tall figure of a man in a frock coat and top hat, walking very slowly through the gardens with sadness and utter dejection stamped across a deathly pale, drawn face. I never 'saw' him as such, as I would normally see another person. But I saw him through my inner eye. At first I thought he might have been one of the earlier Dukes of Sutherland, who owned the estate. Subsequently though I have felt that maybe he was unrelated to the family but so totally immersed in that negativity we shared that he was perhaps its perpetrator.

Another place where someone could have contributed at least partially to the atmosphere might well be Newstead Abbey, situated between Nottingham and Mansfield. Standing in its own extensive parkland and gardens with lakes and wooded areas, it also possesses a village in the grounds, a church and mansion. Previously an Augustinian priory, the abbey passed into the Byron family shortly after Henry VIII's Dissolution of the Monasteries in 1538. During the early part of the 19th century, it was reputedly the setting where the poet Lord Byron practised 'the Black Arts'! However, one or two of the ghosts seen there to this day were well ensconced long before he was even born.

One such spirit is that of the evil Black Friar, whose ominous appearance usually foretold some crisis, generally death, in the Byron family. He even attended the wedding, so it is said, of the poet to Annabella Milbanke. More recently, a workman who saw the ghost collapsed and died. Sir John, a Byron of an earlier age, is believed to step out of the frame of his portrait, wander down a passage, sit in a chair and read a book. A white lady too has been seen quite often – the spirit perhaps of Sophia Hyatt, a deaf mute in love with Byron, who was killed in a coaching mishap.

Boswain, the poet's pet dog is said to still run around the grounds and has also appeared on the abbey roof. Obviously a versatile animal!

During a recent visit to Newstead Abbey, Jan Jordan and three fellow psychics actually saw the Black Friar – and all have lived to tell the story!

"But we didn't see the White Lady," she informed me with a slight hint of disappointment in her voice. "Although they have called the restaurant after her." She then went on; "There's a lake in the grounds with a waterfall and it was in a secret room under the waterfall where Byron used to sit. The atmosphere in there is absolutely fantastic, and there's a profound feeling that you're being watched!"

A very similar feeling was experienced by myself one fine, mellow autumn afternoon when Dilys and I walked up from the village of Birchover, Derbyshire with friends onto Stanton Moor. According to Doug Pickford in his excellent book *Magic, Myth And Memories,* this is a deeply spiritual place, its 150 acres being one huge burial site used during 2000-1000 years BC. Here certainly was ground that held feeling, exuding atmosphere at the same time. I felt in awe of the place but certainly not fear, being reassured possibly of our being watched over by some great earth spirit, custodian of all those ancient peoples resting there.

The high point of our expedition was the Bronze Age circle of stones known as 'The Nine Ladies'. These are about 3 feet in height, the diameter of the circle just over 30 feet. Tradition has it that nine young ladies, part of a wedding party who were brash enough to dance there on the Sabbath, were turned to stone as punishment. The story however, could well have had its origins deep in Puritanism as a warning to others.

More recently the site has become associated with modern witchcraft and pagan celebrations, particularly around Midsummer Night. As with many such ancient sites, its original function may well be thrown to conjecture, although we know our forbears had understanding of the changing seasons and an appreciation of the movements of the sun, moon and stars. It is even speculated that these sites were constructed to harness energies for healing the sick, ritualistic fertility, and for the benefit of livestock and crops so that people could live harmoniously with each other and the bounteousness of Mother Earth.

Although Stanton Moor with its richness of fern, heather and copses of windswept trees did feel special, I did think that the power of the Nine Ladies Circle, although still present of

64

course, might well have diminished since former times. Perhaps the old quarrying activities nearby had interfered with those lines of energy that once passed through the circle – although I thought there was quite a strong energy still present in the centre. Doug Pickford suggests that originally there could have been a stone positioned in the middle as a focus for the Summer Solstice.

I discovered that in many areas such as the Derbyshire Peaks where the ancient knowledge and religions with their healing stones, ancient cairns and stone circles held sway for thousands of years, there has in more recent, bigoted times been deliberate vandalism of such sites. One example, alas is the site of the standing stones of Arbor Low Circle, near to Monyash. They have been pushed over – possibly for cleansing reasons in the name of Christianity.

There are examples where the ground can be very emotionally charged, where ghosts or spirits are harboured also, due to a highly dramatic source event. So it is of little surprise that the potential savagery of battle should leave lasting impressions strong enough for periodic re-enactment.

Probably one of the earliest phantom battles took place between Greek and Persian armies over the Marathon Plains. It was first seen shortly after the Greeks proved victorious in the actual battle of Marathon in 490 BC. More well known was the first and one of the bloodiest battles of the English Civil War – Edge Hill, which took place near to Kineton, Warwickshire in 1642, involving over 14,000 men. Many times since the event, visitors to the area have witnessed the ghostly armies of Charles I and Parliament in combat replay in the sky at night over the original battlefield! The sight was seen initially by some of the people who had taken part in the battle, who actually saw themselves in the action replay! Although the spectacle has not been witnessed for quite a while now, people still sense an eerie, shivery feeling in the locality, as though they are being closely scrutinised by many dead soldiers. One person, it was reported quite recently, has seen what he thought was a young Royalist officer dying under a hedge.

Shortly after June 15th 1815 when Napoleon was finally defeated at the Battle of Waterloo, the citizens of Vervier in Belgium were audience to a repeat performance as phantom cavalry and fierce cannon-fire billowed across the sky.

Understandable they may be, these re-enactments, bearing in mind the extreme emotions undergone at such tense moments when everyone is on a knife-edge, in a 'kill or be killed' situation. But I think it is still puzzling why some phantom battles are fought in the skies over their geographical point of origin rather than on the ground.

On Midsummer Eve 1735 a phantom army was first seen on Souter Fell, near to the village of Scales and north of the now Keswick to Penrith road, in the Lake District. Besides turning out to be an anniversary manifestation, it was in a sense very untypical. The original witness, a farm-hand, reported seeing a large army of soldiers moving in an east to west direction. Being local, he knew that Souter Fell was over 900ft in height with extremely steep sides, impossible for such an army to have access to. When people heard his story he became the target of ridicule. Typical of course, he was regarded as a simple country yokel! One of the main protagonists was his employer, a Mr Lancaster. But on Midsummer Eve two years later, Mr Lancaster too saw the same phantom army with cavalry, then infantry, travelling in the same direction as before, and disappearing into the mountainside. Like his farmhand, he also became an object of scornful amusement.

However on Midsummer Eve 1745, Mr Lancaster made certain he had a number of witnesses with him who all saw the spectral army, this time with carriages. Next day they climbed up Souter Fell hoping to find footprints, hoof-marks and wheel-tracks. There was nothing to suggest that such a physical entity as an army had passed through the area at all! And after about ten years' re-run the phenomenon was not seen again.

Interestingly, because the terrain was so inaccessible to such an army in the first place, it has been suggested that this 'replay' could have moved from its original (unknown) location.

There is an echo of even earlier times in the sightings by many alarmed ramblers of a phantom Roman legion on the march, crossing the heights of the Derbyshire Peak District between Hope and Glossop, where there was the important military fort of Melandra. The ancient route can still be traced on foot through the deep, dark heather, but none of the local rangers have seen the soldiers, although they have encountered the shock and distress of people who claim to have experienced such an encounter. The list of such 'historical' sightings is endless.

In *The Paranormal – A Guide To The Unexplained* by Anthony North, the author recounts a day in 1953 when a heating engineer, Harry Martindale, a dependable, no-nonsense kind of man, was working in the cellar beneath the Treasurer's House, in the cathedral city of York. He witnessed a company of about sixteen Roman soldiers appear through a wall, slouch across the cellar and disappear through the wall opposite. Apart from when they were walking through a trench that was dug across their path, he noticed they were visible only from the knees up, as though they were walking on ground more than a foot below the existing floor level. He also observed that they were dressed in the Roman soldier's normal short 'skirts' and leather helmets and were armed with long spears and short swords. They also carried round shields.

At the time, sceptics said that working alone in a cellar in a city dripping with history might well have primed Martindale's imagination. Considering his temperament, that seemed unlikely. Some historical experts questioned his claim that the soldiers carried round shields, but it was known that a Roman road had existed beneath the cellar. The sighting, however, was witnessed again several years later, by two archeologists, subsequent research showing that when the Sixth Legion moved out of York during the 4th century, the auxiliaries who replaced them did indeed carry round shields.

Dilys commented in this connection how essential it is when any ghostly encounter takes place for the facts to be reported as accurately as possible.

"It is important if you have witnessed something to say exactly what you saw, not to make it into something you thought it was or thought it should have been. Subsequent research will almost always prove you right."

I paid a visit just recently to what is probably one of the bleakest sites on the Staffordshire Moorlands - the Mermaid's Pool, called Black Meer, on Morridge Moor near to Leek. Having looked at photographs, I had assumed it to be fairly large in size. But on this particular wintry morning, having had great difficulty opening the car door thanks to the gale force winds and heavy rain, in order to get out, cross the road and look over the fence, I was surprised to find the pool little more than a duck pond in area, its black waters agitatedly rippling because of the inclement weather conditions.

Naturally, the mermaid was not to be seen on such a morning but the area did feel strangely special. It was here that according to local tradition, several murders have been committed over the years and the mermaid has the dire reputation of suddenly appearing, snatching her hapless victims from the bank and dragging them down into the acidic waters to drown. It is claimed that a spectral arm has been seen reaching up from the waters of the pool. Small wonder that people avoid actually walking past the spot after dark.

There are other pools in the Derbyshire Peak district that are supposed to have resident mermaids. A number of people say they have seen them. Below Kinder Downfall for example, those who visit the Mermaid's Pool there and actually watch the mermaid bathing may be endowed with the gift of immortality. Or alternatively, according to her mood they could end up suffering the same fate as the unsuspecting victims on Morridge Moor.

Belief in mermaid-type forms goes as far back as to when Celtic goddesses, along with other deities, were widely worshipped across this area. Also, these mermaid pools could possibly have been used for ritual human sacrifice.

During World War Two the reservoirs of Derwent and Howden were used for low-flying practice runs by the famous 617 Squadron, prior to their attacking the German Mohne and Eder dams in 1943 using the famous 'bouncing bomb'. Although there were no casualties during these 'rehearsals', there have since been widespread reports of phantom aircraft sightings over the area. Probably the most well known is that of a Lancaster bomber seen flying silently over nearby Ladybower reservoir on moonlight nights, then suddenly disappearing. Such a plane had actually crashed in the area early in 1945 and the crew, mainly Australian, were killed. It was at a recent Open Day at St. Edward's Church, Leek that Dilys and I encountered an elderly gentleman who pointed out a plaque that bore the names of several air-crews of planes that had crashed in the Peak district, during World War Two. Among those listed were the crew of a German Junkers as well as the young Australians who had perished in their

Lancaster so far from home, whom he said he had actually known.

Bircham Newton Airfield, near Kings Lynn, Norfolk was built at the start of World War One, left derelict at the end of hostilities, then brought back into commission for World War Two. Stationed there were personnel from the Royal Air Force, Royal Canadian Air Force and the Royal Australian Air Force.

Following World War Two the site was partly used for industrial training, and the officers' mess became a hotel. Behind the hotel were two squash courts, one of which was said to be haunted. Two men were engaged in a game there when they became aware that they were being watched from a walkway overlooking the court, by a man in RAF uniform. Then they saw him walk along towards a doorway at the far end and disappear.

Aware of the area's history – and the fact that someone had previously seen a similar figure walk through a wall built after World War Two – they decided to leave a tape recorder in the court overnight, locking the place up with the only remaining key. When the tape was played they hardly believed their ears, for it revealed all the indications of an air-base on full alert. Voices of men and women giving and receiving orders, directions, sounds of machinery, an aircraft flying over, plus strange, unearthly sounds, and the ordinary activities of men playing squash were heard.

Subsequently, the tape and recorder were closely examined by BBC engineers, who could find no fault with the equipment. The actual tape had not been used before, so there could not have been any sound 'overlap'. Routine checking in other directions showed that no aircraft had flown over the vicinity that night. It was also unlikely that anything could have been picked up externally, as the walls of the court were several inches in thickness.

The BBC decided to do an investigation into the haunting and one of their reporters spent a night in the squash court in question armed with a tape recorder, which switched itself off at 12.30AM for no apparent reason. The reporter said that she experienced a feeling of intense cold in there and that she heard doors banging.

I can remember the case being featured on television and vividly recollect the few seconds they played of the (original?) tape – voices, calls and laughter of the spectral squash players. It sounded very uncanny, so much so that instinct told me it just could not have been anything 'fixed'.

A medium who visited the court picked up that a Anson aircraft had crashed nearby during World War Two, killing the crew of three, records showing this to be true. But she went on to say that the airmen were still hanging around because they had not realised that they were dead.

A popular belief is that where a place is haunted, the spirit energy is somehow held within the fabric of the immediate surroundings and every so often, for some reason, that energy is released either as an unseen presence, an aroma, something visible, or as a sound. This may seem plausible considering wood, bricks and mortar, trees and the ground. Add to these even rocks, a placid lake or pool, and seashore.

But how, I wondered, would the theory hold up in regard to phantom ships? Is it possible for something as turbulent and changing as the sea itself to hold spirit energy? Going back to schoolboy physics, true even in wood, bricks and mortar, rocks and metal, there is constant movement to do with molecular energy. But that is miniscule by comparison. Yet, as it was pointed out to me, there is something common to all places claimed to be haunted. It is one of the basic elements – air.

Phantom ships have been seen all over the world, around the British coast being no exception. It was off Dunnose Point, close to Ventor, Isle of Wight that *HMS Eurydice* sank during atrocious weather in March, 1878. There were only two people who survived the catastrophe, while 300 naval cadets were drowned. Since that time a number of people have claimed sightings of the phantom ship, floundering off the Point.

A friend of mine recently told me about a ghost ship he saw one summer when he was wandering along the coast-line near Minehead, in Somerset. Seated on a rock on top of the cliffs, he saw a ship suddenly come out of the mist and thought 'Aha! A training-ship!' So he decided he'd hurry back to the harbour in order to see her actually come in. Keeping an eye on the vessel, he retraced his steps along the beach and it followed him, quite close in. He told me he noticed who was on board and the type of craft she was – a tops'l schooner, and wooden. He still thought it was a training-ship, or else a privately owned vessel of some significance. Then it vanished, going into another bank of mist or fog. It never appeared again.

Calling in at the harbour master's office he asked if they were expecting any vessels. They were not! So he went off, did some research, and found the only comparable craft were French, called *La Belle Poule* and *L'Etoile*. They were, he discovered, the only schooners that worked in the Bristol Channel at that particular time. But neither was operating there that day.

He then recalled that there had been only three crew members, and that they had all been wearing flat caps. If it had been a training-ship, there would have been considerably more people on board. What was even odder was that he recollected there had been no life-belts. Intrigued, he tried to discover more and found out that there had been several ships that did not return to Minehead after World War One. The only one vessel of that description that did not fail to return to her home port was *The Periton* – a tops'l schooner.

On the night of 17th November, 1840 the paddle-steamer *City of Bristol*, crossing the Irish Sea from Waterford to Rhosili Bay on the Gower Peninsula, South Wales in a fearsome gale, lost course and ran aground, breaking in two just short of her destination. On board were seventeen crew members, several passengers and a cargo of pigs and cattle in pens. Similar to the *HMS Eurydice* disaster, there were only two survivors, one of which managed to hang onto the tail of one of the cattle as it swam to the shore.

Over the years, the wreck of the ship was buried in sand then exposed again, as the sea displayed its various temperaments. But when it became exposed in October 1990, the *Daily Mirror* reported that villagers near to the scene were being disturbed nightly by the sight and sound of spectral hands – those of men, women and a dead child – tapping on their windows and depriving them of sleep.

Thinking on the point raised earlier about our seeing ghosts in public places and probably not realising it (at least, to begin with), Mel Howlett recalled an occasion when he had had such an experience.

"The place where it happened was Porlock Bay, near the village of Porlock Weir in Somerset. In the mid-1960s I used to do a lot of beach walking, and going along a ridge of shingle, which drops down by about 30 degrees into the sea, I became aware of three men and a boy walking just below and slightly ahead of me. I took no notice of them at first because you're passing people all the time along the beach in various states of dress and undress. What made me look again was that they appeared very ragged, and one of the men seemed to be wearing breeches which I thought a bit unusual. One, I think, was a coloured man although I wasn't sure.

73

"I walked on, and they crossed in front of me and went down into what is called the Marsh Field, which lies inside the shingle bank. I carried on, looked down, and they'd gone. Again, I didn't take much notice until I was talking to a local JP who was also a collector of folklore and stories, about these people who'd vanished. He became quite interested.

"He told me the bodies of three men and a boy were once washed up on the beach. It was not known whether or not they were Christians. Of course, in the early 1700s they didn't bury anyone unless they were Christians in consecrated ground. So these unfortunate victims were buried pretty well near to where they were found in Marsh Field, and three large stones were set into the shingle bank to mark their graves. That of the boy remained unmarked. Apparently their spirits have frequently been seen coming up from the sea by a number of people."

What the experts say

Paul: Why is it, do you think, some old battles have been seen in action replay above the original sites where they were fought?

Dilys: Ground and walls – things of earth - we may tend to think of as bench-marks for retaining energy. But they're all elements, so the element of air is just as much a retaining factor as the ground. And so, too, is water.

Simon: Thinking of air, there could be a lot happening when such events are seen. Atmospheric conditions may just be right at certain times, humidity, moisture in the air for example.

Dilys: Like when people used to see a rainbow and didn't understand why it was there until they discovered it was refracted light, water and rain. So we, at the present time, don't know much about seeing things of the paranormal until someone actually finds out the 'scientific' explanation.

Simon: Maybe that's another question people should ask about hauntings – it might be very important to note the weather factor when researching these things.

Dilys: Yes. Make a record of it. We all know about the coldness and temperature fluctuations, but the fact that it might have been raining could be just as important. You may find there are other things present such as electric storms or a build-up of electricity, that certain atmospheric conditions do figure a lot in these things. When you read stories about terrible disasters, wrecks and so on being seen again they hardly ever happen on bright summer days. They generally occur on dark, stormy nights, like when the wrecks happened.

Simon: That's another thing about a lot of ghost stories. They always have thunder and lightning in them, so creating a very spooky atmosphere.

Dilys: So you could even query – 'Which came first? The ghost or the thunder? Or, the thunder or the ghost?'

Simon: I think that connection with static electricity and electro-magnetism does make it easier to shift levels, as it were. Taking refracted light and other things we've just discussed into consideration, something on the horizon – like a hill – may appear higher or lower than it actually is.

Paul: Yes. A very basic example, by partly submerging a straight stick in a bucket of water, it appears to bend.

Simon: This might be a whole new area of investigation that's never really been explored.

Paul: Do you think so-called 'mermaid pools' exude a strange atmosphere?

Simon: Every place exudes atmosphere. With mermaid pools you've got water as well as the Celtic connection.

Dilys: You can generally find that you don't have to have a large pool. Even a spring can have a good deal of atmosphere.

Simon: That can be good or bad. I don't buy into this idea that the mermaid just sits there and murders people. We'd hear a lot more about it if that sort of thing was really going on. People build up an awful lot of folklore around just the atmosphere.

Dilys: In olden days before people had cars, by the time they got up to these remote places they were probably suffering from exhaustion, hypothermia and hallucinating, so they would've 'seen' things anyway. It's not as if these pools are just round the corner.

Simon: Also, if activities were taking place and the site needed to be protected from interference, those in the know would have intimidated people, scared off those who weren't aware of what was going on. Maybe even threatened them with murder, or told them murder had happened.

Dilys: It's a question of faith and daring, courage even. A visit to, or involvement with such sites could have been frightening. An initiation, a trial to pass through perhaps, even if one is afraid. In the old mythologies, people had to go through trials. If they were ready to pass through they would have elevated themselves to new awareness, and this can be applied to any form of spirit activity, because you are prepared for it to be very frightening. But if you are prepared to go through with it, it ceases to be frightening because you are aware of it.

Simon: And talking about ghosts being connected to deaths or causing them – yes, certainly, some people would be scared to death, quite literally by seeing a ghost. But it isn't seeing the ghost that kills them it is their reaction, their own fear.

Dilys: If you were a member of a primitive society you would be very aware of things like this and just take them for granted. When told that something was frightening, that there was a spirit in the thunder for instance, such peoples accept it as natural along with everything else. Then they start to

76

worship it, along with the sun, moon and so on, because they recognise and respect the power.

Paul: What about the atmosphere on Stanton Moor and the Nine Ladies Circle? That felt special to me and probably has done for a long time. Can atmospheres mellow?

Simon: There are still people who go up there now and work with that energy. But there might be less of an awareness by some of us, perhaps, we don't have that resonance with it any more.

Dilys: It might be different if you were up on the lonely moors alone in the middle of night, as opposed to just sitting on the stones having a picnic with friends on a sunny day.

Simon: I think people can destroy the sacredness of a site. But not completely damage it.

Dilys: Like water wearing away a rock, it might take a long time. But that sort of usage of it, that casual demeaning has the same result in all spirit work. If you demean or take it for granted as part of every day, you can lose your respect for it. And if that happens it is withdrawn from you to a certain extent.

Simon: Mind you, it goes a lot deeper than just saying a place has an atmosphere or doesn't.

Dilys: Yes, stones don't do a lot for me personally, but if the energy of a site wanted to connect it wouldn't matter whether the stones were still there or not.

Simon: That's right.

Dilys: If the stones have been knocked over and people have put graffiti on them we're inclined to say "Poor old stones! They've lost their magical power!" But the stones are not the energy. The energy, the power is still there. And you can't touch it.

Simon: The stones are just marking the areas of energy, the sites. I think the stones have misled the Christians, who have believed that by knocking them down they'd done a good job, and that the energies would've gone away. They've left sites alone after that. But the site just carries on.

Dilys: The energies in the earth, the earth spirits and the other worlds are still there. Spirit is the 5th Element, which we cannot see or touch. (The other four, of course, being earth, air, fire and water). The whole point here is that people do relate to things. They say it's a haunted object, a haunted house, or haunted ground. But they are trying, by doing this, to find a way of actually getting control. What they are talking about is something they can't relate to anyway, that's too frightening on its own. So they break it down. Regarding the sites, some might say, "Oh, it's a wonderful, powerful place, or it was until it lost its energy. We had a picnic there!" – or something similar. But the site is, as you say, Simon, only a way of marking something perhaps we can't take as what it really is.

5

Poltergeists, Haunted Objects and Smells

One could say that many hauntings focused on buildings, areas or objects tend to last for long periods of time. Conversely, a poltergeist (from the German meaning 'noisy spirit') might manifest itself at a location for a much shorter period of time, but because of its apparent destructive and spectacular nature – where household effects like crockery, ornaments and furniture can be thrown around and smashed – it tends to receive more publicity than most other paranormal phenomena.

Poltergeists have sometimes been defined as 'haunted people'. An external entity – as some believe – latches on to a particular person, through which it can be activated. The phenomena could even be internally generated (psychokinetically) by someone affected by stress, even though they might not be physically responsible for activity that could ensue. I say "might not", but as such activity is known to evolve around an age range from puberty to about thirty years of age (even older in some cases), investigators have known older children to be knowingly responsible for poltergeist-type activity without actual poltergeist presence as a hoax. But investigators have also encountered many cases where they were not.

Some years ago, Mel Howlett was teaching in Warwickshire.

"A pupil in one of my classes was very distressed, finding life growing up extremely difficult. Her mother had died, her father had remarried and she couldn't get on at all with her step-mother," he said. "Her father led an extremely busy life running his pub and restaurant.

"She was away from school for about a week and on her return told the teachers, 'I've been getting into trouble for trashing my room when I didn't do it. Not at all! And my dad took me to the doctor who said there was nothing wrong with me and that I was faking and being wilfully naughty. I'm not being naughty, though my room's been a mess!'

"There was a parents' evening a fortnight later, and I spoke to her father. I said that she was really trying hard at school, though I understood she'd been a bit naughty at home.

'Naughty?' he said. 'She's only trashed the Bar several times!'

"'She didn't mention that,' I replied. 'She just told me she'd been accused of damaging her room.'

"'You can come down if it happens again,' he said. 'And see for yourself.'

"He rang me about three weeks later.

"'You say she does no damage,' he exclaimed. 'Well, you should see what a state the place is in. My wife and I were in bed when it happened. It can't be my wife – so it's got to be her!'

"I went down. In the Bar there were glasses smashed, pictures smashed, tomato ketchup all down the walls. The whole place looked like a battlefield.

"'Look at that!' her father said. 'It's going to cost me hundreds!'

"I told him he'd got a real problem on his hands. It looked like poltergeist activity.

"'That's what some of the neighbours have said,' he replied.

"So I suggested that in order to get to the root of the problem, after clearing the Bar for the night (after washing up, etc.), he sealed all the doors and windows – Sellotape would do – and got a witness if he liked. He did all that.

"Four or five days later, the place was absolutely trashed again. But the seal was discovered to be still intact.

"'If your daughter had done this,' I told him, 'she'd have broken those seals to get in.' He then apologised to her.

"I got talking to the daughter, quietly and on her own, about the manifestations. Her father was quite right, she was 'doing it' but not in a physical way. She told me she would get feelings of terrible, pent-up frustration that nearly blew off the top of her head. She said they built up and built up till they 'burst', only then allowing her to go to sleep.

"She'd had several of these attacks, obviously. So I started to work with her very, very gently, teaching her some techniques to help her deal with them. And all the trouble went away."

Mel continued. "A professional lady I knew lived with her son who was in his early twenties. The house was subject to very aggressive poltergeist activity. The walls seemed to run with gallons of water, carpets were ruined time and again. In fact the downstairs front room was so bad it was completely uninhabitable.

"Visiting the house, after checking there were no other presences, I measured their energy levels. Those of the son were wildly fluctuating, very erratic. Having talked to him two or three times I found that he too had these explosions of energy within him, welling up almost uncontrollably. When he felt them coming on, they coincided with the attacks on the house.

"It emerged that since the death of his father he'd had an intense relationship with his mother, so much so he found it extremely difficult to leave home, and to form a relationship with the opposite sex. He still tended to cling to his mother, who was trying gently to ease him out, and to ease him into adulthood.

"What Amy, my wife, and I did was to teach him techniques in how to dissipate the energy. We gave him an analogy that what he had within him was a positive charge that needed to be discharged, and that if it wasn't it would do damage to himself and the environment. So as soon as he felt these attacks building up, he had simply to stamp them into the ground, clap his hands and shake his arms and feet. And it worked.

"Later he got a job he liked in a different town and became more settled. And of course the poltergeist activity in his mother's house ceased."

Prior to these two genuine poltergeist cases, I mentioned that investigators have sometimes found children have been responsible for poltergeist-type activity. There have been examples where, for various reasons, people have actually 'created' ghosts too. Any one of us achieve this if we allow ourselves to do so, and not necessarily as a hoax. In some over-panic situation, for example, an old barn can look 'spooky' in moonlight. So can oddly shaped bushes and trees. After a hot summer's day a house will contract in the cool of the night, sometimes creaking as much as a wooden-walled sailing-ship at sea. All sorts of sounds can easily be conjured up and misinterpreted by vulnerable imagination. Dust-sheets over items of furniture suddenly take on the appearance of weird presences. But as any ghost hunter or other psychic investigator knows, dealing with such things it is a matter of discipline and the possession of that healthy balance of scepticism and open-mindedness.

Back in the 18th century, smugglers would spread tales of haunted bays, inlets and caves to keep away prying eyes from their illegal activities. Indeed *'A little suggestion goes a long way'* so the saying goes – as in the early 1970s, when a journalist wrote about the phantom vicar he had located in the area of Wapping Docks, London. Very many local people were to write in afterwards with details of sightings they had encountered of the same 'Vicar of Wapping'. But only the journalist knew at the time that this phantom was of his own making - a hoax! As the response from readers had been so overwhelming, Colin Wilson, author of many books on the paranormal, arranged an experiment. A volunteer was hypnotised into thinking that she would actually see 'the Vicar' at a certain location at a particular time. Later, she was to claim she had done so.

Probably one of the most remarkable examples of 'creating' a ghost (or spirit) again took place in the early 1970s, this time in Toronto, Canada. Calling him 'Philip', the research team concerned decided to put their heads together and invent a phantom, creating his whole background and story themselves. So Philip became an English 17th century aristocrat who, although married, had a torrid love affair with a gypsy-girl. Eventually accused of witchcraft, she was burned at the stake while Philip silently stood by and let it happen. This, the team decided, would be reason enough for his 'ghost' to wander around the castle on his estate, desperately seeking forgiveness for his cowardice.

Thus having created Philip's existence and history, the team attempted to make contact through a series of seances. This proved futile because of their intensely serious application. But in 1973 their approach became more relaxed and cheerful. Their method of communication was through rapping in song. Philip seemed to respond to certain songs and to his name. Again, through rapping, he answered 'yes' or 'no' in line with the 'life' that had been devised for him.

From there, Philip progressed to being able to move a table on which members of the research team had placed their hands, sometimes quite spectacularly across the room. It was by rappings and movement of the table that he was to go on local television the following year, though he was invisible of course. On camera, one of the research team then told Philip that he was really just a figment of their joint imagination. Suddenly, he ceased to exist, but was later 'recreated', after his research team had decided to believe in him once more.

Viewing old furniture at auction, for sale in a shop, or at an open-air market we naturally have our likes and dislikes, according to taste. There may be something we go for immediately, a deal quickly and warmly arrived at. Sometimes though we hesitate, despite there being just the place for that 17th century dark oak chest, or 18th century brass-faced grandfather clock. We may sense a strange, non-pleasant 'feel' about what would otherwise have been an ideal buy – and we allow the opportunity to become the new owner to pass.

One of the many methods a psychic may work with is psychometry, where simply by touching an object, the waves and vibrations still around it can be picked up. Even people who are not very psychic can do this.

Dilys told me about two rings of particular interest that she once bought at different times. The first was a Victorian mourning ring purchased at an antique jewellery fair, with the name of the person it commemorated engraved on it. Surprisingly, she found it joyous and uplifting to wear and still has it. For a while she was in possession of a huge ceremonial ring made of silver, inlaid with mother of pearl and some kind of black stone. Too large for her hand, it had once belonged to an associate of Aleister Crowley, and was reputed to have been used in magical rituals. You might think that the vibrations it issued would have been strangely frightening and foreboding yet Dilys found it a very dull, boring object, with no character at all.

Many things like paintings, *objets d'art*, pieces of furniture and curios have debatably been suspected of harbouring – not poltergeist activity as such – but ghosts, spirits or simply even negative energies, that could have a profound influence on their owners over several generations. Whether or not the object in question gets moved over great distances makes little difference.

In 1982 a Mrs Spence from Las Vegas was paying her Auntie Jean a visit in Greater Manchester, when her fancy turned to a small 'olde worlde' pottery cottage container which had been in the family for years. Auntie Jean presented it to her niece as a gift and back in Las Vegas, the pottery cottage was used for keeping small things in, such as stamps, pens, pencils, etc. Not long afterwards, a weird shadow was seen loitering against a bathroom door. Then more than once, Mrs Spence encountered the ghost of a man passing through the house. As there had been no such presences before, the pottery cottage became suspect as the source of the hauntings.

When calling on Mrs Spence, her daughter Billie would often say how much she liked the object, despite one time experiencing a tremendous 'chill' come over her, although it was a hot summer's day. Another time, she saw the ghost of the man standing next to her. Although surprised she was not scared, especially when her mother told her that no harm had been done since the pottery cottage's arrival from Greater Manchester, England.

Mrs Spence wanted Billie to be the cottage's next owner, though she too had witnessed the weird shadow and seen the ghostly man pass through her house. She too had kept small things in the pottery cottage until, attempting to check the manifestations, she had the bright idea of leaving it empty. This seemed to do the job. Instead of having to wander about, she assumed, the entity, or entities that apparently 'inhabited' it had somewhere to live once more.

The writer Denys Watkins-Pitchard told of the occasion when his grandfather, a man of the cloth, bought a mummified foot from an antique shop in Northampton. The following night the foot, in its box, was locked away in the attic. During that night Amy, a younger member of the family had a dream where a young girl had her foot ceremoniously amputated by some priests. Waking up horrified, Amy got out of bed and went on to the landing. There she encountered the box - which she knew her grandfather had had locked away – complete with foot sticking out! Soon afterwards – probably wisely - it was committed to consecrated ground.

Helena, a beautician in her late thirties, told me about a recent purchase she had made. Given here in her own words, her story was highly dramatic and I listened spellbound!

"I bought a statuette of a gladiator from a local craft fair. I thought 'Oh, I've got to have that. It's lovely. All in marble!'

"Temporarily, I put him in the box-room. Then I saw my little dog on the landing outside shortly after, and he was shaking. And I said to him:

"'What's up? Stop shaking, 'cos you're scaring me!'

"Next thing, he started barking. But I thought nothing more of it.

"Anyway I started having problems with my husband. He comes out with all this rubbish. 'I'm a man!' and 'You're the woman. You're supposed to do as you're told!' And I'm thinking to myself that there's something wrong here.

"'We don't live in Roman times!' I said to him.

"Eventually, I went to see my mum and explained things were going from bad to worse and she asked me if I'd bought anything recently. I told her I'd bought this marble statuette and she advised me solemnly to get rid of it. I did, and after that there were no more problems. I threw it into the nearest skip!

"I'm definitely of the opinion that ghosts, spirits, or whatever can get in certain things and play havoc with your life. That's why I think a lot of people have got to be careful when they buy antiques. Depending on what they buy."

Another large category of haunted objects includes, of course, all the things that make up our methods of transport. Once there were horse-drawn carts, wagons and coaches – many of which, as we have already seen, have passed into traditional ghostly folklore. But thanks to a constant update we can now include more modern transportation like cycles, motorbikes, cars, lorries, motor coaches and aircraft. No doubt some time in the not too far distant future we will be hearing reports of haunted spacecraft!

Physical objects such as World War Two aircraft housed in museums may be haunted. In some of the former, crew members have been eerily seen still on board or on the other hand, the crafts can take the form of actual phantoms themselves, like the Lancaster bomber still seen over Ladybower in Derbyshire. Along haunted roads at night, the sudden appearance of a 'ghost' vehicle seemingly heading straight for someone driving in the opposite direction has been the cause of many accidents over time, while phantom cyclists and motorcyclists have been known to take many an unwary traveller by surprise.

All forms of transport, particularly if over remote areas or long distances, can give us feelings of awareness, expectation and destiny. Whether our journey involves our first flight to New York or a day's coach-trip to the coast it is a cause for heightened emotion. If something occurs that we had not expected, such as a tragic accident, then that can become an even more heightened focus in itself, perhaps opening up the possibility of the event being 'recorded' for periodic action-replay for some considerable time in the future.

Roads, as we know, are often settings for paranormal activities. Old roads, even if they no longer exist physically, still have their ghosts, some going back a very long way. Dilys told me that while doing research for a series she was writing of guidebooks to North Wales, she came across an old tradition stating that, although Boadicea was Queen of the Iceni, which was a British tribe in the south of England, she had in fact been a Druid. When she died in battle against the Romans, it was assumed that her remains were interred under what is now one of London's main railway-stations.

But folklore suggests that after hostilities, her remains were spirited away by her followers along the old road up through the Welsh Marches for burial on Anglesey, the sacred isle of the Druids. Alas, the Romans had already sacked the island, so it is not known where Boadicea's final resting-place actually is. But during her research Dilys had talked to several people living alongside the route of the old road, who claimed to have periodically heard the galloping of horses and the clatter of the chariot wheels of the phantom 'hearse', on its way to Anglesey.

And what about phantom trains? Arnold Ridley's famous play *The Ghost Train* encapsulated all the potential for thrill and spooky mystery that might be encountered not only on the 'Ghost Train' in the fairground but on some deserted, weed-infested station platform in the middle of the night. For example, the shade of an old signalman seen working high in his box, or that of the lamplighter going about his nightly duties, the villagers nearby who have heard distant whistles and the sound of steam engines passing by, during the small hours.

The present Tay rail bridge is said to be haunted by the night train from Edinburgh, which in December 1879 plunged into the River Tay below during a storm that had demolished the central section of a previous structure that had stood on the same site. The crew and seventy-eight passengers were killed. Rumour had it that for years afterwards the train had been seen, lights ablaze, on the anniversary of the catastrophe, to cross halfway over the bridge then disappear.

The phantom form of Abraham Lincoln's funeral train was said to have been seen making its way from Washington back to Illinois on the anniversary of his death, when it had taken the body of the assassinated president to its final resting-place. Each time the phantom train passed through a station, it was said the clocks would stop. Sometimes, a group of skeletal musicians, so it is claimed, has been seen performing on one of the wagons. (Lincoln himself was never seen aboard, although he has been seen on a number of occasions in the White House).

Ghostly aromas are not as common as actual entity appearances. Neither can they be recorded audibly nor by video camera. They are said to occur either as a phenomenon in its own right, such as the smell of incense in abbey ruins, where it has not been burned for hundreds of years, or they precede an actual appearance of a spirit, remaining until the spirit disappears.

Generally the more pleasant aromas indicate a happier presence, even though there may be other, more maligned spirits in the same location.

Situated in Erdington, near to Sutton Coldfield, West Midlands at Shepherd's Green House, Victorian in origin, the face of a nun has been seen peering out from an attic window. A voice is heard and there is an aroma of sweet-smelling honeysuckle. In Warstone Lane Cemetery in the same area, it is said that a white lady in a crinoline dress has been seen wandering. Who she is, or her connection with the location, is unknown. Witnesses have reported that when she appears she is accompanied by a smell of pear-drops.

At Sutton Hall, Derbyshire built in 1720, later belonging to Richard Arkwright whose father invented the Spinning Jenny, workmen in the cellars have detected the smell of tobacco smoke as well as hearing footsteps, but there have been no actual sightings. The same smell has also been detected in the Brining Room in Balsover Castle, also in Derbyshire, the 17th century home built for the Cavendish family on the site of a Norman castle. It also has a number of residential ghosts. Another source of aroma is the Star Chamber at the same location which according to one of the custodians, exudes the smell of strong cucumber; while at Seymours Restaurant, in Derby, a grey lady appears with the more pleasant sensation of lavender. The staff have seen her several times and say that the perfume precedes her appearance and that she always smiles. At the White Lion, on the Ashbourne Road also in Derby, previously a coaching inn from the 17th century with its residential ghosts, customers have detected the smell of violets.

In *Dancing With The Dark*, a book of true paranormal encounters compiled by Stephen Jones, Peter Haining, a well known journalist, editor, and himself a prolific anthologist of ghost and horror stories, relates how in early summer each year, he and his family have experienced the smell of wood smoke in the house they have occupied in for some considerable time. The property, timber-framed, with some outbuildings, dates back to the 16th century and is situated in a small village in Suffolk. It once housed the stewards of the local landowners who lived in a nearby Elizabethan manor house.

They only became fully aware of the strange phenomenon however, when one evening Peter's wife Philippa was sitting in their bedroom, reading. In one of the walls was an interior window that overlooked the landing. Suddenly her eye was caught by something going past the window – a person with long, flowing hair. For a moment she thought it was her daughter, then realised that she was actually on her own in the house. But she did not feel in the least afraid.

After making enquiries, particularly in the village itself, Peter and Philippa discovered that a number of older people, whose forbears had once been employed at their house as servants many years previous had heard talk of their also witnessing the figure. Yet, they too, had not felt any unease about it.

The source of the wood smoke smell, so it was said, went back to the early 19th century, when French prisoners from the Napoleonic wars were brought to the area and billeted in the outbuildings to their house. They were put to useful work on the land and to property maintenance, being well treated. But one day in June of a particular year there was a fire at the house and, trapped in a room, one of the prisoners died.

Every year since, over a few days prior to June 6th, the smell of wood smoke has increased, suddenly ceasing on that date – the same date when Philippa saw the figure with long, flowing hair go past the interior window and disappear.

I was surprised at the number of people who told me about ghostly visitations involving the smell of flowers. A woman who had lived in an old farmhouse that dated back to the 14th century reported the periodic fragrance of lavender and lemon although no ghost was ever actually seen. Lavender seems to be the most fashionable ghostly fragrance, probably I imagine, because lavender flowers were used in many connections in daily life in previous centuries.

Generally the scents do seem to have pleasant associations but I came across one story where the scent of flowers was linked with tragedy. Although it actually appears over and over in folklore tales set in some castle – any castle – I think it is a good one and worth re-telling here. A young bride eagerly took part in a game of hide-and-seek in a large house, concealing herself in a wooden chest that could only be opened from the outside. Discovered fifty years later, her remains in her wedding-dress still clutched a bouquet of lily-of-the-valley, the fragrance of which people had sensed each time her hapless ghost had walked the gallery.

It was in the early hours of one night in late winter twenty years ago, that I myself experienced a haunting involving the sense of smell. I awoke to an atmosphere in my bedroom supercharged with cold and a strong smell of sulphur. In spite of the darkness I saw quite plainly, facing the door, sideways on, a bent figure in black rags. It was hideously ugly, I was able to note, despite the dark hood it wore. Male or female, I could not tell. Perhaps androgenous. It did not seem to matter. And my reaction? Horror, fear? No, just sheer surprise! After watching it for a few seconds I reached out to switch on the bedside lamp. My visitor had disappeared, so had the smell of sulphur and then after about a minute, the cold. After about a quarter of an hour, I switched off the lamp and soon returned to sleep.

I certainly did not dream the incident, though that instinctive, gut feeling was my only proof. Plus the fact that I remember it so distinctly. We might all experience horrific dreams at times but they tend to get forgotten about. So was some malevolent, demonic spirit 'trying it on' on this occasion? Strange, because I was going through a relatively happy, healthy, unstressed period of life at the time, something else that I clearly remember. Oh, and one last point. My visitor never came again.

What the experts say

Paul: Have you ever been asked to deal with a poltergeist, Simon?

Simon: I haven't, no. But there was one case I went to where a bathroom had been set on fire, more likely by a disgruntled spirit than a poltergeist, which tends to evolve more from unsettled children perhaps. Thinking about it though, it's so easy for an investigator to say, "Ah, we've found the answer. That's all sorted out now! The children did it!" The trouble is that a lot of investigators are not psychics. They're just looking at the physical evidence rather than that presented by the psychic evidence. It's true that children can do things when something else has taken over, but it's a different sort of energy. Sometimes a child can pick up a stone and throw it, without knowing what they are doing.

Paul: Could the girl that Mel Howlett mentioned have unconsciously trashed her bedroom, even though she was not responsible for the mess in the bar?

Simon: It doesn't sound like it in this instance. In some cases, it could be a possibility. I mean when someone accuses you of doing something, there may be an unconscious reaction – you do it anyway.

Dilys: As an investigator I always say one should always look first for natural causes, physical phenomena, rather than supernatural. I think 90% of most manifestations of this kind are explainable from natural causes, including here the various forms of mental imbalance we usually call mental illness. I have encountered people who have done things but who've said they couldn't help themselves, or they didn't do it themselves, or that they couldn't remember doing it. Also those who had felt like the girl did. In fact, I've experienced that myself to some extent, actually filling up with energy enough to explode. Training as an investigator or psychic, you have to learn to control this kind of thing through the disciplines, and work at it constantly.

Paul: Have either of you come across objects with a strange feeling about them?

Simon: Yes, loads! Like antique furniture. When you think about it, it's perfectly normal for most things to absorb energies over time. Unless it happens to be brand new, it'll have something attached to it, even if it's boring, or nothing much has happened to it. Every single object has its own energy.

Dilys: A psychic I worked with was giving a demonstration of psychometry and someone from the audience handed her a ring made of silver. Although it was brand new, by gently touching it she was able to pick up from it the people who had actually mined the silver.

Simon: The idea of being drawn to an object is fascinating because it could possibly indicate a past life, or reminders of furniture from a past life. From a church if one had been, say, a priest.

Dilys: The same with old places. Just think of the number of visitors to places one has heard say, "Oh, I really do feel at home here," even though they may never have been there before in this life.

Paul: And what about ghostly smells, aromas?

Simon: One of the things that amused me was the smell of cucumber you mentioned. I'm sure there are plenty of smells and other things we take for granted. We don't even think 'Oh, that's a spirit!'

Dilys: Smells can sometimes be symptomatic of illness.

Paul: Yes, I was reading about Catharine Mompesson, the Rector's wife at Eyam, in Derbyshire at the time of the Great Plague. She remarked on the beautifully sweet aroma she could smell after weeks of helping the unfortunate plague victims of the village. Her husband knew at once that she herself had contracted the plague, because that happened to be one of the first recognisable symptoms – smelling a sweet smell.

Dilys: Even with the most weird of smells though, most of them can be physically explained away. It's the ones that can't that need to be investigated further.

Simon: I still feel it's too easy to say just find a physical explanation.

Dilys: Well, I'd say clear the physical first. Then see what's left.

Paul: What about the 'thing' I encountered in my bedroom? Any comments?

Simon: Any number of reasons!

Dilys: Of course a psychiatrist would say, "Oh, yes? What were you worrying about?" or "What had precipitated it?" in a case like this. But there is a lot more to it than that. If you are investigating, you cannot be dogmatic or dismissive. Some might suggest you were externalising your worries, fears or problems. Someone else might say it was an elemental, or a demon passing through, or that you invented or dreamed it.

Paul: I didn't dream it. I can't offer proof, except gut feeling that I didn't.

Dilys: But so would anyone else say who'd claimed to have had such an experience. I think we're given experiences to test us, but never ones we can't cope with, even though we may think we can't. Maybe you were being shown dimensions you weren't aware of at the time.

Simon: I agree. All you can say is, "I think that was my experience. This is what happened to me."

Dilys: The most important thing about it is that although you didn't find it pleasant, you faced it and you coped. A lot of spirits are bullies, and if you turn and face them the majority will go away.

6
The Tools Of Their Trade

Throughout history people have lived with ghosts and have been aware of other worlds. But many, apart from having holy water about the house, a crucifix on the wall and garlic for possible protection against the odd vampire, have no idea how to cope with hauntings or spirits, though they know that all sorts of remedies exist in traditional folklore. Some of the old practices were carried out to enable the spirit to go safely on its way.

Many civilisations have recognised this necessity. In Ancient Egypt for instance, food and personal possessions were put into the tombs of kings to help them on their journey to the next life. Sometimes their servants were killed and sealed in with them for the same purpose. Some tribes of North American Indians used to burn everything that had belonged to the departed person, including his tepee. Closer to home and more modern times, mirrors were covered, neighbours would draw their curtains on the day of the funeral – not only to show respect but to shut out the spirit, encouraging it to go on its way. Another well known superstition is the nailing of a horse-shoe over an external door so that no spirit can enter - and of course there are numerous other examples.

If there is a ghostly presence in the house most people won't understand why it is there, be it malevolent, mischievous or simply happy and contented. And they will generally assume they have no other option than simply to put up with it. If it is a happy sort of 'spook', they are fortunate. But to look the other way when faced with whatever kind of presence is not always the solution. Nor is to cut and run from terrifying situations always practical in terms of one's financial situation. The answer? Many seek the expertise of the psychic, or some other kind of investigator.

The investigator has various briefs to carry out. He or she is there for the person who has called them in initially, to identify the problem and deal as effectively as possible to bring respite from the supposed haunting and to help the spirit or entity to pass safely on to wider horizons.

The investigator needs a balanced approach – a healthy scepticism and an open mind as to what he might find. But by open mind, this does not mean having all mental channels open, going in naively unprotected, otherwise he could well come away from the scene of a haunting having been invaded by whatever entity or entities he has encountered, particularly if of a mischievous or malevolent nature.

Different churches have their own attitudes and methods of dealing with the spirit world and the investigators their different methods too. I discovered that in general they do not trespass on each other's methods but respect them and refrain from comment, publicly anyway.

Some follow procedures that are more explainable in physical terms, whereas others follow more spiritual, intuitive methods of approach. Most investigators feel that they need to invoke some prayer or protection in the work they do. Jan Jordan is typical in that, although she always wears a crucifix, she relies very much on her spirit guides for protection during an investigation.

And contrary to how the large screen industry would have us believe, real-life genuine 'ghost-hunters' do not assume a high profile and go crashing in, as the film *Ghostbusters* implies. They operate very much low profile, with quiet efficiency. I was interested to discover how they applied their different methods, and in this chapter we will be hearing how several different practitioners work in this field.

Mel Howlett's method of contacting spirits is mainly through dowsing, which he has practised throughout many parts of the world. Mel works in conjunction with his wife Amy, who is a medium. When I asked for his comments on how he went about his work he was helpful and extremely informative.

"It means perceiving that which is beyond one's own immediate sensory experience," he said. "And if one receives the data or information by other methods one can immediately construe as coming through the five senses."

Most practitioners, regardless of method, seem to approach their work in this way. Since Mel is a dowser he began by explaining how the dowsing process works.

"If you wanted to find potable water, you can dowse over a field, and although you can't see the stream 6ft under your feet, your body has sufficient sensory equipment to tell you – the dowser – in which direction it is flowing and its depth. The same can be applied to finding oil, minerals, finding lost objects and tracking people. My field of dowsing entails response to human energy, putting all antennae into the air, extra-sensory perception, gathering bits of information that might escape the human eye but be present in the vibrations of energy lines."

"Applying this to a house for example, you can find out if it is sited on any of these energy lines, and whether the house is suffering from geopathic stress, which is if it is being affected by the various types of lines. The dowser will codify them by colour or number scale. Some energies can be dangerous or harmful to human-beings and will be coded red or orange. To check that a house is balanced, he will dowse each room separately or the house as a whole, on scale with human compatibility. Then he can say whether or not the house is 99-100% safe. Usually in one or two rooms, you find that the energies are harmful to human-beings. Things like black streams of water deep under the structure can have a negative effect on the body."

To me there sounded nothing supernatural at all about this. But when I asked about dowsing a house with 'presences', he said that that was a different matter.

"It could have belonged once to someone who never wanted anyone else to encroach on what had been their territory for thirty to forty years, was still very possessive and disapproving of any changes a new owner might have brought. The first indication to the latter that something was wrong could be the feeling that someone was standing behind them, disapproving of what's going on. Or it might be a tap on the shoulder, or a grunt."

"So when the current owners ring you up for help and you arrive," I said to Mel "what's the first thing you do?"

"You explain to them that there are different kinds of haunting, then sit down and take out your dowsing equipment," he replied. "I use the full range – wooden rod, or slender forked twig, brass swivel (hand-held), pendulum, crystal, or bobber. Any one can be used to give a 'yes' or a 'no'."

"Would the forked twig be of hazel?" I wondered, since I had heard this somewhere.

"Not necessarily," Mel said. "So long as it is something supple. Put a twist into it so that it's held in a tension, so the least movement in your hand will flip it up or down. Or you can get some springy wire, put a loop in and hold in tension. The loop will move this way or that, likewise for a 'yes' or a 'no'."

I was shown how a pendulum was held slightly in front of the dowser, completely still, before an initial question was asked of the supposed presence. Such as: 'Are you male?

Female? etc', and the pendulum would move. Whether clockwise gives the positive answer, and the anti-clockwise direction gives the negative, or vice versa, depends on the individual dowser.

"The question is put mentally, an active interrogative, very focused," Mel continued. "Very disciplined. I say disciplined, because you can get ambiguous answers. You can get yourself into very serious trouble if you're not careful. So being very single-minded and using old dowsing techniques, you ask: 'Are there any presences in this house?' You'll get a 'yes' or a 'no'.

If 'Yes' you ask permission on behalf of the current owner whatever question you want to ask. For example: 'How far back in the past?' 'How long did you live in the house?' Name, date of birth, etc. Then you get more focused on feelings. The more focused you become on the situation, the quicker the answers come back."

"All the same," he added "the dowsing part of our work is slower, with its 'yes' and 'no's, whereas Amy can get, via automatic hand-writing, answers quite quickly.

'My name is Emma.' I was born at X in 1806, etc.'

"When doing automatic handwriting Amy can 'fall' into it fairly quickly. By closing her eyes and concentrating, she can allow her hand to be completely taken over so much so that the writing assumes the characters of the individual in question. But you've got to be intelligent about this sort of thing, because unless it is understood it's just so much psycho-babble, ecstatic utterance.

"It can become focused if it's directed by an entity, which is why you get such clear glimpses of the past – an entity, or specific character who wants to give you information relevant to the situation with which you are dealing. Amy and I don't come across any archetypal figures like Napoleon or Nell Gwynne. Often it's someone born in a terraced house in a small town, who lived and worked there for over seventy years, did their shopping in the High Street and hardly went anywhere else. Just ordinary people coping with cancer when there was no hope, or dying of gangrene – this at a time when the doctor charged 1/6d, too large a proportion of a week's wages; ordinary people relying on home remedies that were near useless who want to talk to you about their experiences.

"Once they've received your empathy and understanding, care and guidance they can often be pushed into the right arms, the right hands, these being people on the other side whose job it is to welcome those who've come through the death experience."

Remembering that ghosts are as diverse in character as they were when physically present in this world, and bearing in mind Dilys comment that "some ghosts – if you met them as people – you'd run a mile", I asked Mel if he and Amy had ever dealt with a really difficult case.

"Yes," he replied. "And I agree there are some really vicious hauntings of people you'd want nothing to do with when they were alive let alone when they're dead and which, if you'll let them, will invade.

"I'm not going to mention any names," Mel told me "but a flat we came to know was haunted by the spirit of a vicious old gentleman who'd led a life of crime. He had never been found out but now that his time had come he was too frightened 'to die'. When a very sensitive, artistic lady moved into the flat he started not only to resent her but tried to take her over. It began by her feeling that someone was in bed with her, and trying to interfere with her. Other times she found she was being jostled and overpowered by his presence and his fetid breath! In dire straits, she called in the Church. The place was exorcised – to no avail. Parapsychologists and mediums were also called in, but nothing was achieved.

"So the lady wrote to Amy and myself. We discovered, as others had, that we were dealing with a powerful, evil entity, someone who'd gone through the death experience as such but had no intention of shifting on to graduate, mature, or see himself in terms of a larger, wider existence.

"Amy and I showed her how to freeze him out of her mind and not be so receptive, necessary because she was such a warm, loving person. The battle went on and on! We got in touch with his family, only to find they had all passed on but all the same, were in spirit desperately wanting to break through, to help him. We got his parents to 'go' to him, and eventually we got him to tell us his point of view. We got in touch with as many people we could who wanted to help, and told him his parents would forgive him and take his hand and guide him through to the next stage. He wouldn't have any of it.

"Amy and I travelled home but I'll never forget that, two or three nights later we had a full display of his fireworks, a full display of his malevolent intent. No way could we rest, that night."

"Where were you both when this happened?" I asked him.

"In a cottage, a few miles outside Leek, in Staffordshire," came the answer. "And the flat was down on the South coast."

Mel must have spotted the slightly incredulous look on my face.

"To a spirit things like distance and time mean nothing," I was informed. This of course, jogged my memory about ghosts or entities showing little respect regarding our own, more physical world.

"By then," Mel continued, "we knew that neither of us, the Church ministers who had been approached, nor all the sincere measures offered were going to do any good with this one. So we concentrated on the lady (the real-life occupier of the flat), trying to get her to mentally shut down, to close him off. We were to work on her for some time.

"Eventually, she wrote back to us saying she'd had a measure of success but she was unable to keep it up for long. And every time she opened up, he got in. He was so powerful in fact, that he was getting her to drink whiskey, eat meat (she was a vegetarian), and was getting her to do everything that was within his personality but not within hers. In other words, she was being slowly possessed.

"In dowsing, if you say 'I'm going to do that,' you don't have to do it. The intent to do it has done it. That's what dowsers call 'the Dowser's Intent'. As long as the original intent is genuine, that is sufficient. You have got to the stage where you believe that something will be so. But you have to get your client, or patient to go along with that too. And if you can't do it, or they're stuck with a belief system that won't enable them to do it, then the miracle won't happen."

'For the moment, so much for the lady,' I thought. 'But what about the entity?'

"Amy and I felt that this vicious, but immature entity would not accept help for a very, very long time – perhaps years," said Mel. "And probably not before he'd gone through other, successive occupants of that particular flat."

Doug and Hilary Pickford are another husband-and-wife team of investigators who are called out frequently in confidence by people who trust them "not to spread it about that we have a problem!" Doug told me over the phone that when he and Hilary - both partners in mediumship - arrive at a property, it usually takes them between half-an-hour and an hour to get the sense of the place, having gathered any necessary information from the owners and through mind-dowsing, using either a pendulum or dowsing rod as back-up.

"It's a matter of deciding whether the problem is of a spiritual or physical aspect," Doug went on. "If there is a presence, contact is made with the entity and Hilary and I try to help it on its way."

Up to now I thought this seemed a somewhat familiar approach. But what he had to say next was to *really* grab my attention.

"Sometimes, if it's physical," Doug continued, "the problem may well lie with the property owners themselves. Fear of the unknown, etc. So it's necessary to remove all such worries with sympathy and a bit of 'self-help' psychology."

He was to recall an occasion when he and Hilary were called out to a farm. They were told of what the owners thought was a strange, unpleasant atmosphere in one of the old outbuildings where - so it was discovered – animals, in the past, had been slaughtered. By applying their dowsing techniques, they were able to trace an underground stream beneath the foundations which had caused the energies of the animals to remain fixed in the building. So Doug and Hilary were intent on assuring the owners that all would be well.

"And simply because they accepted this," Doug concluded, "the energies in the building were actually dissipated."

It was after she had just spent a busy day recently at a Psychic Fayre that I managed to put a few questions to Fabia, a lady in her mid-forties, as she was preparing to leave for home.

'How did *she* get called out to a case?' I wondered.

"Usually by word of mouth," she answered, in her calm, relaxing, slightly husky voice. "From people who've had problems before or who've got them now. They get talking, asking others. So I get called in by recommendation."

"Having listened to a householder telling you of the problem initially, do you actually prepare yourself, as a form of protection, before 'going in'?" I asked.

"I have a whole day to prepare myself, mentally and physically," she said. "To have a good sleep the night before is most essential, so that you're not edgy or low in spirit. I always have a purifying bath and then meditate and really try and get myself calm before I set out."

I then asked Fabia if there was anything special, in the way of tools that she took with her.

"I have several sorts of crystals I use for this particular kind of work," she replied, "also a kit consisting of oils, candles, various herbs and a tray – using everything I take, making sure nothing is used belonging to the householder or person I'm going to. When I actually start to work," she continued, "I'm thoroughly calm, aware I'm taking nothing of my own life into the house. Thanks to my guides and helpers, I also feel very, very strong. But really the main thing is to be totally calm and clear before going in."

"In this sort of work, I think you're generally performing a service for people who are very worried and distraught because something's been happening in a house they've occupied for a while. If the house is 'new', a lot of people walking along the spiritual path these days just don't want anything left over in the house such as 'atmosphere' or problems the previous owners had. Many people moving into older property ask me along to check that everything is clean, free from negativity, and has a nice vibration before they move in. Something else they ask to be checked is the presence of any ley lines running through the property. If so, there would be certain items of furniture they would not want to put across, or place near them.

"Sometimes, in a property where you've got children who aren't sleeping, it could be something they've picked up while being out and about, so it's just a matter of making sure the children are safe," she added.

"Could you tell me about any particularly interesting case you've dealt with?" I asked her.

She thought for a moment, unconsciously pushing back a lock of brown hair, her dark blue eyes suddenly focusing.

"There was a young girl – aged about 16 – who was being threatened in her bedroom. Initially, it was thought she was suffering from nightmares. But after some time and a particularly horrendous screaming session, she would not return to her bedroom, refusing even to go upstairs at all. After a family conference over the matter, I was approached. I talked to the young girl, who described the entity, or thing that had been threatening her with ever-increasing viciousness over time, as being very tall and wearing a black cloak which had silver markings on the epaulets.

"At first I tried to cleanse the room and the whole of the upstairs area, then asked the entity to move on, just on a person-to-person basis, saying it wasn't welcome in the house, because it had been causing disruption. Afterwards, I told the family the reason I had used this method was because it was not too harsh. But on leaving, I asked them to contact me if there were any more problems. Usually, an entity will move on if they realise they have been causing harm or upset."

"Anyway after that things got worse. Another entity had come into the scenario! This one was only as high as the bed, but waking the girl up, and trying to get her to go to where the taller entity was standing in the doorway. Obviously, because I had previously put a circle of force to keep it out, the latter entity couldn't enter but it was sending something else in to bring the young girl out."

"I realised a more drastic solution was called for. I asked the family to leave the house and stay away for a day, deciding to tackle the problem on a one-to-one level with the taller entity in the cloak. I had done some research and having checked again with the girl's description, discovered that he was Germanic, and the silver markings on the epaulets of his cloak were swastikas. In fact, he was from the SS! The smaller entity, which I dealt with first, was a Germanic dwarf."

"I know this sounds ridiculous," Fabia told me, "but some research I found going way back, suggested the best way to deal with this sort of entity was to make a bowl full of proper porridge, leaving it out overnight when the entity arrives, then throwing it out in the morning. So we tried - and it worked!"

" 'We'?" I queried, enthralled by the story.

"Yes, I sometimes have help from a fellow psychic" she confirmed, "and sometimes I help her."

"Next morning we went in, started at the farthest point in the house from the girl's bedroom and literally blessed every door, window, every mirror, sending the taller entity in front of us, all the way. But when we got to the bottom of the stairs it had put up a wall of 'sludge', cold, strong. A really horrific coldness. Regardless, we carried on all the way up the stairs, blessing/clearing all the windows up through the house, the entity still before us. The bedrooms we also cleansed, but as we approached the young girl's room the cold suddenly turned to an absolutely horrendous heat! The entity had already been asked to go, and to visualise the portal I had mentally provided for it to go through. To no avail. This time I told it *very* firmly it was to move on, that it was no longer wanted on this level and that there would be someone to meet it on the other side, to send it on."

"I had the impression that nothing was happening, and the room was just getting hotter. Then very *forcibly* I repeated myself. Suddenly, the heat disappeared quite dramatically, the bowl and candlestick we had on the tray suddenly shattering, as the temperature returned to normal. The impact absolutely frightened the life out of us! It can be very dangerous to both carry a tray and be concentrating at the same time. That's why my friend was carrying the tray, providing back-up. Anyway, two heads are always better than one! And because we'd been through the house, completely cleansing and blessing it, when the family came back, they immediately felt the difference in the whole atmosphere!"

"Why do you think the Germanic spirits had been drawn to the house in the first place?" I asked Fabia.

"Well, I can only surmise, but they could have been connected with some World War Two artefacts that were in the house. I think several new items had recently been added to the collection," came the information. "But these had all been cleansed, as a matter of course, when we went through the property."

"What happened eventually to the artefacts?" I queried.

"They were taken away," she replied. "And donated to a museum, I think."

Before I had developed enough interest in the subject of ghosts to begin researching for this book, I had accompanied Dilys a few times when she was called out to deal with manifestations. In the first case coldness had been reported in the bedroom of a flat and a 'ghostly woman' had been seen a number of times. A young couple, Ed and Sharmain, lived in the 1960's block and it was Sharmain who had seen the cold outline of the woman and told Dilys about it. However, she said she did not believe in spirits and was inclined to brazen the whole thing out. When Ed was woken by it one night though, it was a different matter. He had been scared out of his wits and refused to sleep in the room again, so Shamain had been forced to take action. She got in touch with Dilys and asked her to visit the flat.

On our arrival, Dilys was shown the room. Left alone, mysteriously to me she identified a small area that she said, felt quite cold. Apparently, this was the corner of the bedroom where the spirit had appeared and I remember that Dilys lit a candle, placing it on the small bedside cabinet. I did not know the significance of this. After meditating for a short while, she somehow picked up the spirit of a very upset teenage girl, who was simply distraught with temper because she had not been able to have things her own way on some previous occasion. There was also a small dog spirit present, Dilys thought. Eventually she asked Ed to open the front door. Then she walked slowly towards it, apparently with the spirit of the teenage girl going before her.

On the second occasion Dilys had already spoken to Megan Ryan, owner of a Victorian terraced house, who was experiencing frightening visitations from an invisible presence which, entering her bedroom at night, would 'sit' on the side of her bed. Dilys had picked up the spirit and said she thought it was a soldier or someone wearing an army greatcoat. She also thought the spirit was someone known to Megan – perhaps a grandfather.

On arriving at the house, we did not get as far as the bedroom before Dilys stopped in the kitchen and identified a very cold spot at one side of the fireplace. She thought there was a presence there of a woman. Megan agreed that when she sat in that area, she always found it icily cold even though there was a glowing fire and the rest of the room was warm.

Dilys thought it was an older woman – nothing to do with the soldier – who had always sat at that spot and had been reluctant to leave the house when the time came.

Again the procedure seemed to involve a candle being lit, and flowers being placed, and of course the open door. When she had dealt with the kitchen and the spirit of the woman had left safely, Dilys was about to go up to the bedroom but Megan revealed that since speaking to her, she had remembered an uncle who had been a soldier who had died very young in World War Two – and she had realised he was coming to offer her help with a problem that was worrying her. Once she realised this, the spirit had departed and not returned. The bedroom was now clear of spirit activity – Dilys went up and confirmed this.

When I came to write this book I asked her to explain exactly what she had been doing on these occasions. She said:

"I had to deal with trapped spirits who were unable to pass from these particular places for some reason. Generally I would begin by identifying the spirit and, as a medium, trying to make contact with it and finding out why it was still there. In most cases – and these were what I would call reasonably typical – once contact has been made I can communicate with the spirit and explain to it that all is well and it is time to move on. In both these cases I was able to do this. But for a spirit to leave you usually need some sort of door – even if only symbolically – so I asked for the front door of the place to be opened.

"Then I encouraged the spirit to go to the door and leave, accompanying it and sending it to the Light where it rightfully belongs now. I will also say prayers for the spirit if it seems to need them. The candles burning and flowers placed are to represent purification and cleansing and also, I feel, as a mark of respect for the departed spirit, in the same way one sends flowers at a funeral. You did not mention it but I always carry my crucifix with me also, as both protection and so that the occasion is blessed. I have to add that when I am called in to deal with supposed ghosts or hauntings I also carry with me other things that might be needed – like salt, sage and even a vial of holy water. Mostly one does not need to use them but sometimes in difficult cases, the place may need to be cleansed and purified thoroughly after the spirit has been dealt with.

"I rely very much on the protection and help of my own particular spiritual guides to help me deal as wisely and effectively as I can at any given time, remembering that each individual case is different. You can never lump 'hauntings' or infestations together because even though some of them are very similar, each one is unique.

"I think it is important to mention that, when called to cases of this kind, one is only an instrument that can be used to help sort out the problem. I'm very aware, as most others involved in this work are, that one needs far deeper resources than a human-being possesses. That's where the help and strength of spirits and guides comes in. That is also why it is important to be free of one's own personal hang-ups, like negativity and ego, as much as possible."

*

Since this chapter is filled with expert comment I am going to finish with a few observations of my own. Up to a few years ago, I had thought that getting rid of a ghost or rogue spirit simply meant asking in a representative of the Church, to wave a few lighted candles around a haunted property and say a prayer. The thing would then presumably be cast into the Abyss. As my interest in the paranormal grew however, my sights became somewhat broadened. But it was only when preparing this book that I really came to appreciate the depth and intensity of the work involved when one is an investigator, psychic or otherwise.

Although all those I have spoken to have their slightly different approaches, there seems to be a common aim - to help any trapped spirit to pass on. What interests me is that if a spirit is distressed and too terrified to go and the investigator claims to make contact with its relatives who may have already passed on for their help in the situation, I cannot help thinking it could well have been the relatives who caused the spirit to have problems when they were alive in the first place. As the saying goes: '*We do not choose our relatives.*'

Interviewing the investigators, I have certainly been struck by their keenness, dedication and in spite of their high success rate, their quiet humility. Also, despite the lengths that some of them go to in protecting themselves, their work still carries a considerable risk. A job for the experts obviously. And *not* for those who choose to dabble.

7
On the Ghost Trail

In order to acquire some practical experience of what the investigator is likely to come up against, I decided to plunge in at the deep end and spend a day 'in the field' with an expert, my colleague and 'resident consultant' Simon Tansley. Simon is in his early forties. He is what is called 'clairsentient' – which simply means being aware of the spirit world - and he has operated in the Staffordshire-Derbyshire area over a number of years. Before the two of us set out on a case where I would be able to see him at work first hand he explained his approach and technique.

"Generally, I don't go looking for ghosts particularly," he said. "I 'pick up', just get the feeling of a place. Sometimes there are lines – what I call ghost lines – energy lines really, and the ghosts will move up and down them."

I recollected him mentioning energy lines with regard to Lowes Cottage so I asked him if a ghost line was the same as a ley line. He did not think this was quite so, that a ley line was more to do with the earth, whereas a ghost line is more intangible, being connected to spirit.

He reckoned that a ley line could be moved round the outside of a house, whereas to move a spirit or ghost line was a bit more difficult.

"Which would come first then," I wondered, "the ghost line or the house?"

"The line, always," he replied. "It's a matter of how the earth is made up, and which different sorts of energies can be attracted. Sometimes there can be interference from mineworkings, quarrying and so on."

From the detailed information Mel Howlett had given me, I understood what was meant, though I had not realised before that there was so much influence – whether positive or negative – from the ground beneath our feet.

"Modern houses tend to get built across lines, it seems to me," Simon continued, "and to have a line running through the house can have a detrimental effect. There can be problems when beds are placed across such a line. Negative energies can drain us, for instance, while we're asleep.

"Water too can have an effect on a building – underground streams, wells, stagnant, or even a vortex of, water. These can produce energies coming up through the earth that are detrimental. They can also be power points – positive or negative. Sometimes they're in pairs. Sometimes too, they can be influenced by a person. A different person will have a different power point. That's how a potential power point, or energy, effects the person, the environment."

So how is this sort of invisible influence dealt with? Having lived in a house similarly affected for a while myself I knew how difficult it was – if not impossible – to move the structure, walls or parts of a building to another location.

"With a negative vortex under a house something can be done, at least in the short term," Simon assured me. "It helps to have new ideas, new people who move things about instead of only changing them every twenty or thirty years. I work with Feng Shui and usually recommend – if something has been changed – that it's left in the new position for a lunar month (28 days) for the energies to settle."

"Have you ever come across a negative energy that has fought you, or challenged you in any way?" I asked.

"Challenged, yes!" he replied. "A friend of mine had a house near to Wolverhampton which had old mine-workings underneath."

This seemed to be quite a common problem, I discovered. There had also been mine workings under the disturbed house where I had lived myself for a while.

Simon explained: "My friend told me that a certain room would go cold. He always knew it was a particular day, without looking at a calendar because this happened so regularly. The energies would just build up.

"I decided to divert the line of energy that went under the house round the property by using copper rods. So there I was on my own working in the rain in the back garden, deciding on the exact course the rods should take when the back door just slammed to. I was locked out! Fortunately, I managed to find a window that was not closed properly. But this happened two or three times, as though the negative energies were trying to stop me from doing the job."

Fascinated, I asked him how he positioned the copper rods. Did he dig a trench and place them end-to-end, for instance?

"No," was the answer. "They are knocked into the ground, but with the tops bent over, or even the rods themselves inclined, towards the direction needed to divert the energy. In so doing, the idea is *not* to direct the line of energy into someone else's garden!"

When Simon finished the job at the house he was speaking of, it was reported to feel more positive and the room in question was cured of its bouts of coldness.

"Later, though," he said, "when the next people had moved in, my friend went to see them and found that they had dug over the garden. They mentioned about an unsettling energy prevalent in the house. - obviously, they had dug up the copper rods!"

A similar sort of job was carried out in Tideswell, Derbyshire. A house with a long corridor-type room, which was always cold though the one next to it was just the opposite - warm and cosy - was transformed. Simon dowsed the room in question, and put copper rods around the property outside.

"As far as I know, everything is still going well and that was some time ago," he added. "Regarding ghosts themselves, in those days I tended not to pick up spirits or ghosts as much as I do now. I have never been one for having them exorcised. When contact is made with them, I find they are sometimes irritated by the present owners of the premises, who might have changed everything. They can cause trouble, even set fire to the place, but in some ways, they simply want to be acknowledged. In my work it's almost like making them 'open up', making them realise that there's another, wider world out there."

He detailed an interesting case he attended in Rugeley, South Staffordshire.

"There was this house in which, so the owner told me, there'd been a fire in the bathroom. I could still see some of the scorch marks. The story was that a short, squat candle had mysteriously fallen over. I felt the presence of an old woman about the place, but for the moment she didn't quite relate. There had been an old hovel in the grounds where she had lived many years before. A young lad of about thirteen, who lived locally and who worked with me on this case claimed he 'picked up' and saw the old woman talking and nodding. It turned out that she had been somewhat ostracised by the community at the time yet, ironically, when illness prevailed she was often consulted privately for her cures. When contacted, she just wanted us to say some prayers. Sometimes that is all that is needed. Candles burning or to make a general space for the spirits."

Finally, I asked him if he'd experienced a case where a difficult spirit had followed him home.

"I'm not sure if 'it' has ever followed me home" he replied with hesitation, "but certainly an uncomfortable feeling, sometimes. It's just a matter of finding out what it is and letting it go, one way or the other. Just shutting it out is actually holding on to it, in a way. I like to let it pass through, and investigate it."

So it was agreed that, armed with this basic information, I would accompany Simon one Sunday morning in January. Both clad in thick winter jackets and appropriate footwear, we set out for Brown Edge, in Staffordshire where, when we finally reached our destination, the true warmth of hospitality was reflected in the welcome hot cups of coffee that awaited us as we sat down to be briefed.

"We both seem to be drained," Fleur explained, "particularly me, not feeling well."

"What with health problems – nothing life-threatening, mind," Mike added, "we seem to go from crisis to crisis. Family, things of all sorts in the house going wrong, and having to be fixed. Everything haphazard!"

"Before going to bed," Fleur commented, "we'll often decide to do such-and-such in the morning. But things never turn out that way. We never have the energy."

"And neither do we seem to get the chance to go out and enjoy ourselves!" Mike concluded.

Mike and Fleur, a normally positive married couple in their late thirties, told Simon and myself how their lives had been affected since moving into their home four years ago. And listening to them struck an immediate chord. I too had experienced all the symptoms they had described, whilst living once in a house that had felt 'out-of-focus'. So I was fascinated to see what Simon would find, and ultimately come up with, as a solution.

From the front, Mike and Fleur's mid 20th century bungalow looked very attractive and well maintained, set in established grounds. At the back it was split-level, built into a bank. The lower part of the structure – including garage - had been added in more recent times.

After the initial, helpful chat, we were shown through all the rooms, for Simon to gain some initial assessment as to the feel of the place, with regard to any strong positive or negative lines of energy that might be passing through the building from outside.

Two or three such lines were traced back across the road, entering through the gateway, passing under the building, then away down the garden at the back. Simon, deciding to divert them away from the house, employed his copper rod technique and I assisted him. Sometimes scrambling through large bushes, we knocked them well into the ground. About ten inches long, they were positioned roughly three yards apart, angled slightly in the direction he wanted the lines to flow. This was from the gateway along the inside of the front hedge, running parallel with the road, then turning down by the boundary hedge and to the right, well clear of the bungalow and down into the back garden. He had also taken account of a large chestnut-tree in the front, which he suggested needed pruning. Likewise the overgrown laurel front hedge.

Back indoors Simon undertook a more detailed assessment of the rooms using the Chinese art of Feng Shui. I knew this advocated living in harmony with our natural surroundings by using the more desirable lines of energy (*ch'i*) in the atmosphere and providing guidance on how homes should be orientated, doors and windows placed, rooms and furniture arranged, etc., to avoid harm and negativity. But I was also keen to see how, by manipulating those energies, an ambiance of good health and fortune could be achieved. The *ch'i*, so I learned, should gently flow through each room to promote domestic harmony and prosperity; preferably no room should be overshadowed by the house itself, a southerly aspect to the building being favoured. For a room used mostly in the afternoon, or evening a westerly aspect is recommended.

The kitchen should be at the end of a building. But Mike and Fleur's was no longer, having been usurped by the addition of a passage and stairway down to the (newer) lower level of the bungalow. Having commented that the kitchen 'didn't feel right', Simon suggested hanging crystals (one or two per window), to help lighten the room, break up the energy and spread it out.

Interestingly, Fleur commented that when she and Mike first viewed the property the previous owners had done exactly the same thing, including hanging crystals on the hedge outside. "They had obviously been into Feng Shui," she added. "They were here for seventeen years, so *they* hadn't felt miserable!"

Other suggestions made were to replace the oblong table with an oval or round one; bevel all sharp edges of shelves, etc.; and place rose quartz crystals in odd corners to displace any negative psychic energy that might be present. Simon also came up with the idea of lighting a sage smudge-stick, allowing it to smoulder, the aroma helping to keep the energy moving. Once a year being sufficient.

Next, we went into the entrance-hall. Simon eyed the glass front door, through which the *ch'i* energy was coming in unabated. 'Too much of a good thing?' I wondered.

"Yes, a bit too hectic!" he said. "Ideally, it should be a solid door, allowing the energy in only when it is opened, and a more controlled amount seeping in around it when closed."

"We've never slept well in here," said Mike, as Simon and I entered the main bedroom. And yet, to the unwary eye, it

119

appeared beautifully comfortable. The bed head fitted snugly into a recess along a wall of built-in wardrobes and shelves. The patio windows opened onto a small veranda with a view of several mature trees in the garden below. The feeling was fine and extremely positive, as Simon pointed out. But concerned about a tall Cheval mirror reflecting *ch'i* from the door directly onto the bed, he advised its total removal.

"In a way," he said, "you get two sorts of energy here. Quite a powerful *ch'i*, and an oppressive one. As though your body wants to get on with things inspirational, while your mind says, 'Uh! No thanks!'"

I remembered this tied up with Fleur's earlier remark exactly.

Another reason for shallow sleep, Simon pointed out, was the bed head positioned in the recess. Moving the bed being impractical, he suggested the removal of a lace fringe that was hanging there and pasting stars, or a view of the great outdoors, under the recess for viewing while lying in bed. Recommended also was that the TV should be covered when not in use. There was an aquarium in the bedroom that Mike and Fleur were about to remove and Simon suggested a small water feature (with flowing water) – as a very calming, beneficial replacement. For the same effect, a piece of rose quartz placed on the dressing table to draw away any possible negativity. Someone mentioned amethyst as an alternative. But that would be too energising, they were told.

"It might be beneficial," Simon continued, indicating a small shelf, "to put aventurine, quartz and citrine there, if possible. That would make it a good place to keep money, together with lottery tickets and premium bonds."

'I'll certainly give that a try!' I thought.

Next to the main bedroom was a small, en-suite bathroom. "Not ideal. So keep the connecting door closed," he suggested. Simon further pointed out that there were enough mirrors in there – again – to maintain a plentiful energy flow.

He focused next on a smaller bedroom where, in fascinating contrast, people had experienced deep, oppressive sleep. Again there were built-in cupboards against one wall, this time facing the bed. As recommended for the kitchen, all edges of the woodwork would best be bevelled – no sharp corners - also the cupboards better painted in a pastel shade. The natural wood floor was ideal, but with the addition of a round rug, perhaps. The pictures on the walls seemed large and rather dark so something more spiritual and lighter in tone was suggested, like angels. In an empty drawer under the bed, Simon recommended placing a piece of clear quartz to start lifting the energy, while the cluster-points (of the quartz itself) would keep each other positively energised. He suggested hanging a dream-catcher over the bed. Also, that the burning of candles occasionally would help to further 'focus' the room.

As Mike worked from home, the small bedroom at the front of the property was adapted as a well-equipped office. It was suggested that he put a mirror in the window to reflect the door, thus maintaining energy-flow, to paint the walls yellow or orange – something bright, inspirational – hang a picture and a wall-chart. Simon also remarked to Mike that it might be a good idea not to have his office chair with its back to the door.

Downstairs the extended lounge, although lacking slightly in daylight, felt extremely peaceful.

"But not calming," was Simon's unexpected remark. "There's something not quite right about it."

I was intrigued. There were comfortable easy chairs around, of course. But he indicated the settee facing the fireplace, set under the 'beam' of the small extension that faced the garden. He could feel the whole thing 'pushing down', so he recommended either repositioning the settee, or simply moving it forward slightly from under the 'beam'. The existing blue carpet, he remarked, was fine. But to help 'lift' the atmosphere and the darkness, he went on to suggest placing flowers and house-plants each side of the window of the extension.

Throughout this 'house-search' incidentally, although Simon used a dowser's pendulum at times, it struck me that he seemed to be getting his answers quicker, more by intuition. When asked about this, he said the pendulum was there for precision or confirmation.

Beyond the lounge was a utility room, with a door leading outside. Although Mike and Fleur thought it slightly unsettling, everything seemed fine, indicated by the pet dogs and cats living and sleeping there quite happily.

From there however, a small door led to a hidey-hole beneath the small back bedroom and entrance hall above, where Fleur said she had sometimes heard scurrying footsteps when alone in the bungalow. It was down there that Simon identified a 'presence'. Indeed, I wondered if the two occurrences were connected.

"Maybe," Simon interjected, "because I feel the entity has wanted to be noticed."

Although there seemed to be a feeling of oppression, he recognised down there as certainly 'its' space. But to lift the energy, attracting positivity, his answer was to install a small altar or even a picture of an angel.

"So that the healing, higher energies would help the entity to move on, but in its own time," he confirmed.

On returning to the premises approximately a month later by invitation, we were both immediately struck by the change of atmosphere. Fleur cheerfully informed Simon that her health was now a lot better.

"And visitors have said how the house feels so lovely and friendly now," she added.

The entrance-hall felt just right and so too the kitchen. Not quite all of Simon's recommendations were in place round the house but many certainly were, whilst others were still being processed. The main bedroom was now a good source of sleep both for Mike and Fleur, while the small back bedroom felt a lot better than before. One or two angels had been hung on the walls, and the piece of clear quartz was domiciled in the drawer under the bed.

Fleur's daughter Stacy, however, said that she was aware of a small 'cold area' between the bed and the window. Simon had actually detected it on our previous visit and he now checked it again. His verdict was that the spirit or entity beneath – the one in the hidey-hole - had not yet moved on. Stacey had said she was too scared to go down there. But it was explained to her that as is often the case, the entity seemed more frightening than it actually was because that was its way of protecting itself, and that it was in the process of moving on but taking its time.

"An energy that shouldn't be there," Simon reflected. "Possibly of someone around before the house was built. Someone who hasn't been able to move on until now."

Mike, meanwhile, had cleared some rubbish out of the hidey-hole to create some space for the entity, and put an altar in as had been recommended.

Stacey, in her early twenties, said she was a person who 'saw' things, although vaguely, and was very aware of presences. Interestingly, knowing that she was very psychic, Simon recommended her to visualise a dark-edged circle surrounding a cross. This she could easily summon up as protection against the entity or any other negative forces she might encounter in everyday life.

Being busy people, Mike and Fleur had yet to put Simon's recommendations regarding the small bedroom at the front of the property, used as an office, into place. Downstairs in the lounge though, the atmosphere now felt warm and intimate. Although the large settee was still positioned under the extension 'beam', Fleur assured Simon that it was now brought forward towards the fire when in use.

When we came away he felt pleased, having had the opportunity to revisit the property to see and feel the results of his work for himself. Normally, clients would inform him by phone that things were fine, rather than invite him over again.

Regarding keeping things such as furniture moving regularly about the house as opposed to changing items around every twenty or thirty years, I'm sure we can all think of an example of the latter. As in the property of an elderly relative or, to some extent, even within our own. Things can certainly grow roots if allowed to! Even the owner! Even the house!

Like people, every building has its own basic characteristics - be they pleasant, happy, positive or simply mediocre. Yet it is surprising the number of people who are unaware that they are living in a property that may well be oppressive, 'out of focus', with a high degree of negativity flowing through or rising from the ground beneath. They may feel unwell, staggering from crisis to crisis assuming it is 'just their luck' to be going through such a sticky patch along the odyssey of life. I was one such person, living briefly in that sort of house – until someone put me wise to the fact. Others more enlightened, like Mike and Fleur, call for the services of an investigator.

An elderly person I knew had felt unhappy for years in her 'out of focus' home. Although she had always wanted to leave she had never made the effort, despite opportunities that had come along. She would say resignedly that she'd only leave 'feet first'. Thinking about it now, the reason she did not make that effort was that unconsciously, she had allowed herself to be taken over by the strong negativity in the house.

After she died in hospital the house was occupied by her son and his wife. With new ideas in mind, they made a number of alterations they felt certain had helped to 'lift' the atmosphere of the place. But one evening, so the son claimed, much to his amazement he saw his mother eagerly inspecting some new curtains that had recently been put up in the lounge, running her fingers up and down them to check the quality of the cloth. Then she vanished. Although he did not actually see her again he sensed her strong presence, particularly on the stairs and landing.

Maybe she was keeping an eye on her son, though it seemed strange that despite her longing to leave the house whilst alive, she had returned after having 'died'. Or perhaps she had never really left. Eventually the house was sold, the son and his wife moving to another area, to new jobs. Concerned about his mother, however, they consulted a clairvoyant, who said that it was up to her son, as one of her closest living relatives, to help the spirit of his mother. She advised him what to do. So before finally leaving the house after it had been emptied, he went to the top of the stairs, where he knew his mother was. He gently 'took' her hand and they both walked slowly down to the open front door. Then he said he was suddenly aware of her going out into a most beautiful, warm and radiant light - going 'home'.

8

Part Of The Family

Like Lowes Cottage, older properties whether large or small have seen several generations of ordinary people come and go. They have been settings for domestic dramas of all kinds besides those of births, marriages and deaths. People may have loved their surroundings so much so that there can be happy ghosts content to still potter on into eternity. Someone who lived in a house or worked in a building may have remained or returned to watch over the place, or just to give the current occupants a sense of well-being.

Simon comments: "This type of spirit is usually regarded as a member of the family, as it were. A contented presence who likes to keep an eye on things and offer support. There seem to be many houses with a resident 'happy ghost'. I have spoken to a lot of people who've noticed the smell of pipe-smoke, and that sort of thing. If 'happy ghosts' feel strongly connected to a place they'll stick around, and there's no point in trying to get them to move on.

"For example I was once working in an office in London, and the guy who ran the place asked me to go into the other room. There was the spirit of a woman who spent her time just clearing out the ashes from the old fireplace, and then disappearing again."

"So trying to have her exorcised," I said "would be terrible really, like throwing a harmless soul into the Abyss."

"Yes," Simon responded graphically. "Like throwing your own grandmother onto the street!"

Michael Gater, a relative of mine, was so interested on hearing of my researches that he not only gave me details of some of his own experiences on the phone but later sent me written accounts of the experiences of other family members.

He told me that some years ago when he went to survey an old farmhouse-cum-manor house near the village of Brigstock, in Northamptonshire, he saw from one of the upstairs windows that there was an old man in the old walled garden, merrily picking Brussels sprouts! Since the property was unoccupied Michael went down to investigate, but he could find no trace of the intruder and he discovered that all the doors to the walled garden were securely padlocked.

The inference? Surely that: *'Old gardeners never die. They simply spade away!'*

In his work as a surveyor Michael was ideally placed to visit all sorts of properties, and another friendly ghost he encountered was in another village just outside Northampton.

"I had arranged to inspect a cottage being sold by a theatre nurse from the General Hospital. There was a window in the first floor gable which overlooked the road, and as I drove up I could see someone looking out, but when I knocked on the door I failed to get an answer though I could hear the radio playing and spent some minutes banging on the door, ringing the bell and generally making a lot of noise.

"In the end I drove off, and when I got back into my office my secretary told me the owner had rung up to cancel the appointment as she was involved with a difficult operation. Another appointment was made to inspect the cottage and this time I was let inside straight away. I told the lady I was sure someone had been in the cottage when I called previously, because I had seen them looking out of the gable window.

"'That was our friendly ghost. We call her Annie,' she replied. 'She often looks out of that window when we are out.'

"She said they never felt any fear and had not seen Annie in any other part of the house. They always left the radio playing when they went out though, but not for Annie's benefit – more prosaically, to deter burglars!"

Any kind of property can have its 'happy ghost'. Newly-built houses may unexpectedly have an extra resident, often with no connection to any former building that may have occupied the site while sometimes the extra 'family member' will follow the family around in spirit form.

"We've never seen him but we've been aware of our cheery, bright little spirit for a long time now!" Geoff and Sandra, a couple from Bilston, in South Staffordshire told me. "We can smell cigarette smoke around the house quite often, even though neither of us smokes."

Geoff added, "He's got a mischievous streak about him too," and detailed how ornaments, various *bric a brac* and garden tools were moved about while items of jewellery occasionally went missing – only to turn up again later. The spirit had followed them each time they moved house – except on one occasion, when their new house proved to have an atmosphere that was dark and malevolent. Geoff and Sandra had stayed there for only eight weeks, and there had been no sign of their cheeky little spirit, but it rejoined them 'as large as life' again once they had moved on.

"It's funny," Sandra said, smiling, "even though we've always loved him and so did our children when they were small, we've never bothered to find out just who he is!"

This is often the case. Sheena, the owner of a three-storey business premises in a small North Midlands market town told me, during a recent visit there with Dilys, that a male 'presence' was felt during major alterations a few years ago – usually on the stairs, which originally led to old living-quarters on the top floor.

Instead of feeling afraid, Sheena says that she talks to her 'lodger' – bidding him "Good morning!" or "Goodnight!" She keeps him up with current news, announcing "We've had a new door fixed for you!" or "We've had the rewiring done!" and she reports that: "He seems to fit in very well with the rest of the staff."

Initially, Dilys identified this as an elderly man dressed in a striped shirt, cardigan or waistcoat and baggy trousers, who had possibly been a pharmacist when the premises were used as a chemist's shop, earlier last century. Two young women, members of Sheena's working staff, said they had sometimes felt someone stroking their faces and touching them on the back of their heads when they were using the stairs from the ground floor to the kitchen on the first floor, but on a subsequent visit, Dilys felt that the entity on the stairs was a different one to that of the elderly pharmacist. Possibly that of a younger male employee of about the same era. We could see that there was some restoration work to be done on both floors upstairs. Sheena is planning to develop certain rooms for meditation, which she hopes will keep the spirits or entities present in a positive frame of mind.

As most of the psychics I spoke to will testify, it is the many ordinary, unpretentious people, the neighbourly sort – not normally believing in the paranormal - who quite frequently come up against the fact, and will tell you, that they have a resident ghost. About ten years ago clairvoyant Dawn Rose, based in London, was asked to visit a house in Kew for a party reading of the tarot cards.

"As I went in I was aware of something on the stairs to the right, although I didn't say anything," she told me.

This was on a council estate, probably built in the 1920s/30s. After the readings, when the cards had produced some deeply profound results, she was informed that the house was haunted.

"I know," said Dawn. "I noticed her on the stairs. A little black girl, about five years old."

Her audience was stunned.

"You're absolutely right!" said the woman who lived there. "She's a very happy little soul too. We see her on the stairs and the landing – the children have seen her and they play with her. But she stays on the stairs and never goes anywhere else in the house!"

Dawn thought the spirit had connections with the World War Two era, and she was told that during the 1940s and 1950s the then occupants had actually fostered lots of children, of which the little black girl could well have been one. Personally, I wondered if perhaps she had been illegitimate, her father – an American soldier – having returned to the United States after the War unaware that she had even existed.

There are many instances where an old building, once a large old home, gets converted to business premises such as offices, hotel, residential home, or shop. A testing time for any resident spirit, that might react in one of the following ways:

a) By putting up obstacles to resist change by a creating bad atmosphere, not allowing the business to 'take off'.

b) Simply disappearing in disgust, feeling unwanted.

c) With a feeling of great relief, knowing the place is again part of the warmth and flow of human activity following a lengthy period of neglect.

I came across a very typical example of this last type when Sara, a tall, dark-haired woman in her early forties, enthusiastically described the resident spirit – a young woman - who lives at the back of her hairdresser's salon near to Buxton, in Derbyshire.

"Oh, she's lovely," Sara said. "She sits by the hair-washing bowls and watches what's going on. And then she'll get up and go into the kitchen. Like a white shadow, she is. Slim-built, about 5ft 5 tall, aged 18 or 19. We call her Daisy."

On a visit to have her hair cut, Dilys had actually identified the presence of a girl in a long, probably white dress still lingering in this lovely building. The property, about 300 years old, had been up for sale for a long time prior to Sara purchasing it.

"I tend to go for where I feel at home," she told me. "And when I saw this place I thought, 'This looks nice!' I've been here for four years. I sensed *someone* was around before I actually saw Daisy. I saw her for the first time last year."

"Were you afraid?" I asked her.

"No, because I think she likes company. She seems interested in what goes on. She's been here about two-hundred years, I guess. Where she sits, I know there used to be a window. I think she still loves her home and I don't think she minded the place being done up. If they don't like it, ghosts can put up obstacles, can't they? She's happy, and I'm quite happy to have her. So far, she's been lovely."

During the course of my investigations I have come across several instances of child spirits, ghosts of young people. At a recent Craft Fair held in Hartington, Derbyshire one of the lady stall-holders spoke to me about the resident ghost in her Edwardian house in Longsdon, near Leek, Staffordshire. Some thirty years ago when her son and daughter were 10 and 11, she first became aware that 'someone' was around. One evening a loud bang, some kind of explosion was heard upstairs.

"It looked as though a balloon full of water had been thrown at the bathroom door and burst," she said. "Naturally, I blamed my son and told him off for playing such a silly trick. He said he didn't know anything about it, but the water was there and it had also been thrown at one of the bedroom doors. My daughter was so terrified that night she slept with my husband and myself.

"There was nothing else that happened until a few years ago. I had just woken up one morning when I was aware of a small boy in the bedroom, dressed slightly old-fashioned in a high, fastened-up jacket. He seemed to be moving towards some built-in drawers under a low alcove and I remember being quite concerned that he might bang his head. But he simply disappeared! I just don't know whether the two incidents were connected or not."

When she told me, I felt that they probably were – that the small boy had for some reason been trying to draw attention to himself. His conception of time and space would of course have been different to ours. The lady went on to say that there now seemed to be a feeling of well-being in the house. She thought he was still around and I suggested that she spoke to him, said "Hello!" "Goodnight!" and so on, as Sheena does to the resident spirit in her business premises. She replied that she thought about him quite a lot because her own children had now grown up and left home, and she regarded him as very much 'part of her family'.

Michael Gater sent me the following story about the experiences of his wife Janet, when she was in her teens. She and her younger sister Sheila lived with their parents and two brothers in a terraced house in King Street, Cherry Orchard, Shrewsbury.

"Janet would wake up in the night," Michael wrote, "aware of someone gently holding her hand. She could discern a figure wearing a tweed coat standing by her bed. The face was always in shadow and no other detail could be seen. Janet was never frightened as the figure did not move or do anything other than hold her hand, and she always quickly fell asleep again. Her mother knew about the presence but nothing was ever said to Sheila, who was unaware of the strange figure that appeared to her sister in their bedroom.

"In her letters," Michael continued, "Janet would tell me about her strange visitor whenever he had appeared - in later years, she referred to him as 'Tweed Coat' or 'Old Tweedy'.

"Well, after we were married we lived in Northampton and used to visit her parents on bank holidays. We always slept in another bedroom, except on one occasion when Sheila was away and we slept in her room.

"In the early hours of the morning I was awakened by something moving close to my head. It was as if a bird was fluttering, about to land, or someone with a wash-leather was hitting my head softly. I have to admit I was very frightened, but coming to my senses, I thought a bird or a bat must have fallen down the chimney. When I switched on the light I woke Janet and, searching the room, we found nothing unusual. I was terrified though and refused to sleep in that room ever again.

"We found out that it was only after Sheila herself had married and left home that she was told about 'Old Tweedy'. She had never seen him, but when Janet had left she rearranged the bedroom, found the new position of her bed to be in a cold spot and moved it back to its original place. Sheila thought the cold was due to a draughty window, but that one place in the room was always cold, even in summer.

"Interestingly," Michael concluded, "there was another member of the household who avoided the room – the dog! Although she would enter the other bedrooms, she refused to go into the 'haunted' one. And yet the cat seemed unaware of anything unusual."

Frank Wilbur, a business man in his fifties who lives in the Derbyshire Peak District, told me about his childhood memories connected to a large detached house, alas, long since demolished, that had once been the manse to a Methodist Church in Leek.

"It belonged to my aunt, and was quite old. In fact, when he came to Leek John Wesley used to sleep there. Now and again I'd stay at the house and she would say I'd be sleeping in the same room where he had once slept. It didn't bother me. I was about eleven at the time, and slept soundly. But my aunt and uncle told me that for years they had heard people moving around, particularly in the evening. This was going back before there was television, when they used to play cards a lot. The stairs creaked, and the heavy front door would open and close. I too sensed there were 'things' there. But certainly nothing evil.

"Where we live now – the house originating from the 1900s, with three floors – my wife and I have heard footsteps going down the stairs from the third floor above - where domestic staff would have once lived - early in the morning, at the appropriate time a maid used to get up. But I'm a bit of a cynic. I don't know whether it's partly our own imagination.

"Now, my ex-father-in-law, a dour, matter-of fact sort of man, had a large, rambling garden and said he once saw a girl on a swing there who simply disappeared. I know he definitely wouldn't have made it up, the type of bloke he was. Definitely not normally the sort to seek conversation with anyone."

All kinds of amazing encounters can occur when there is interaction between the 'quick and the dead'. June Colclough from Cheadle, another stall-holder I met at a Craft Fair at Hartington, Derbyshire, talked to me about the occasion her father suffered a heart attack in 1994.

Her mother – who has sensed 'things' all her life – was aware that each Wednesday following (though she did not know the significance of Wednesdays), approaching footsteps heralded the arrival of an entity (unseen) which sat on the edge of her father's bed. This happened over several weeks, and she felt that whatever – or whoever – had visited him had given him healing, because her father made a good recovery.

Sometimes truth is very much stranger than fiction. Gina, whose family originated from Sicily, remembered her aunt, who in her younger days possessed some kind of 'phantom' or 'demon' lover. At half-past midnight she would entertain in traditional fashion a spectral visitor at her villa in Sicily, whom she described as a 'cavalier' type. She could not identify the era to which he belonged, but said he wore some sort of leggings or tights. On a table, she used to set out a glass, a bottle of wine and bread for him. The lady's brother went off to the Second World War, and later the 'cavalier' came to tell her that he had been killed. Gina went on to recount how her aunt's daughter was thrown off a balcony by a malevolent spirit. As she fell, she became aware that someone seemed to have caught hold of her, and she landed safely in the middle of the forecourt below. The 'cavalier' to the rescue perhaps?

Bella, an old friend of mine, hearing I was writing a book about ghosts, rang me up from London the other day with something she thought would be of interest. But I have a special reason for including this most unusual ghost story as 'part of the family', which I hope will soon become apparent.

Bella remembers her father telling her about the time he and several other soldiers were patrolling a section of the fortified coastline on the Isle of Wight, during the early years of World War Two. Naturally, feelings were high as a German invasion was expected at any time.

Bella told me it was very important she set the scene for this tale. Beyond the beach, she said, there were cliffs, along which was a coastal walk. At one end of the section the soldiers were patrolling was an old boathouse, which they used as a shelter and briefing room. At the side of the building there was a slight dip that always held water. This was part of a path that led down from the cliffs. A couple of corrugated iron sheets were put over the dip, making it easier to walk over.

Late one night, Bella's father and two of his mates were in the boathouse when there was the sound of the corrugated iron sheets rattling as someone apparently ran past and down to the beach. Grabbing their rifles, Bella's father and the others rushed outside thinking maybe the invasion had started. They quickly looked around, but saw no-one. Had it been the wind – their imagination? But this happened several times and they started to feel very uneasy so the incident was reported to their Commanding Officer who, the following night (when there happened to be a full moon) deployed the rest of the company round the area – among the sand-dunes, up on the nearby cliffs and anywhere else he could think of.

Everyone in position, they waited tensely. Suddenly the corrugated iron sheets were seen and heard rattling beneath the impact of feet running over them. But to the amazement of the men there was no visible presence there. Even as they watched in disbelief however, they all saw a string of small footprints forming in the sand before their eyes as the invisible 'entity' rushed towards, and seemingly into, the sea. Later they were able to ascertain a set of bare footprints, presumably those of a child or young woman, clearly visible in the sand heading from the path by the boat-house and straight into the sea. They were, however, obliterated by the incoming tide within a few hours – so there was no proof of what they had seen.

"What did they do about it?" I asked Bella, intrigued.

"I remember asking my father that very same question," she answered.

"'Nothing,' was his reply. No-one said another word. Not even the Commanding Officer. What could we have said?

136

Anyway, there were more important things to think about. There was a war on."

I suppose the spirit could well have been that of a happy young woman, running down to the sea as she had in more peaceful times simply to enjoy the pleasures of a moonlight swim. But if the alternative had really been the case, if the story had been based on tragedy and 'she' or 'it' had run into the sea in order to commit suicide, I am hoping that by including this unidentified ghost here we will help her to feel 'part of the family' again, instead of unwanted and despairing.

The most loyal and faithful members of the family are, of course probably pets, and I think their spirits are far more readily accepted as being likely to stay around than those of the human equivalent. Pets are true and loving, and may well feel they want to reassure their owners that all is well after they have departed.

As a nation of pet lovers, we know how much the furry or feathered member of the family loves routine, so cynics may claim it a mere trick of our imagination when, having lost an animal we still hear barking or scratching at the back door at a particular time for a while afterwards, or the cat-flap rattles just at old Deuteronomy's moment to go out, or we hear the late Beauty the Budgie calling to the early morning sparrows long before we human occupants of the house have chosen to get up. But what these cynics may tend to forget is that there has been proved to be strong telepathic links between many pets (particularly cats and dogs) and their owners, not only during their lifetime but also following the deaths of such pets.

During the preparation of this book I spoke to many people who, whether they had owned up to having encountered a 'ghost' or not, nevertheless mentioned almost in passing that they felt some particular pet animal had returned. They had heard it, sensed its presence physically, seen it or felt mentally connected with it, invariably receiving a feeling of well-being and affection from their pet.

There have of course been the traditional stories of well-known animal sightings - Lord Byron's dog Boswain for instance, which as I have mentioned previously, is still apparently to be seen in the vicinity of the family home of Newstead Abbey. And not only dogs and cats make their reappearance in spirit. According to legend, since the late 1940s a phantom butterfly is said to appear routinely at the Theatre Royal, Bath, at every Christmas pantomime.

Mel Howlett mentioned a case he encountered when teaching in Warwickshire, some years ago. A child at the school where he worked knew that, due to serious illness, the much-loved family dog was going to be put to sleep that day. When she got home however, much to her delight and surprise the dog came out to greet her and she felt his fur as he rubbed against her legs. She went upstairs, followed by her faithful pal, to change out of her school uniform, calling to her mother: "I thought you were going to have Brutus put down."

"He was put down," came the quiet reply. "We took him at ten o'clock this morning!"

Regarding pet activity 'beyond the veil', Dilys has told me about various unusual cases she has personally encountered.

"On one occasion I had been invited to spend Boxing Day with some media people who lived in a large, beautiful ground-floor flat on the outskirts of London. Following a leisurely lunch for about twelve people in a room overlooking the garden, while we were talking I said I thought I could see a small animal in spirit form in a corner by one of the patio windows. It probably had been a pet of some kind – black and white but mostly white with black patches, and soft-furred. The family, including two daughters, racked their brains but couldn't think of either a cat or a dog of that description that they had owned.

"As the house was old and converted into flats, they thought it might have belonged to someone else. But I didn't think so. As I concentrated, I was able to describe it a little further. It had, I told them, long floppy ears vaguely like a spaniel. Then one of the girls said: 'Oh, it's Flopsy!'

"Flopsy had apparently been a long-eared rabbit which used to come in from the garden and sit in that particular corner when the girls were very small. It was obviously still present," Dilys said. "Why that animal I didn't know, but it was just happy sitting there."

Dilys also told me about a lady she knew working at a Psychic Fair, who said that her old cat had one day gone off and never come back. Since it was very old, she assumed it had died, though probably naturally. The family didn't know where the body was but the cat had returned in spirit form to the corridors in the house. So much so that the lady and her husband kept falling over him! So she asked Dilys for advice.

Dilys connected with the cat and felt it was in the house because it had felt that was 'home', and being old and feeble it hadn't had the strength to 'leave'. So she suggested to the owner and her husband they held a small ceremony to help their pet depart involving prayers and a lighted candle, opening the door to see it on its way.

"Some time later when we met again," Dilys said, "the lady told me that, following the ceremony they held, it had been really moving. She 'saw' the cat, he came down the stairs proudly with his head up, full of vigour, and walked out into a beautiful light that seemed to gather him up. She said it was one of the most beautiful things she had ever seen."

Another friend, Robert Blakeston, remembered the time he was driving through Ettington in Warwickshire with his young son and daughter seated in the back of the car when they saw a deer that had been knocked down by a vehicle.

"It's alright, Dad!" said his daughter. "It's just got up and got out of the way."

"I stopped the car to have a look," Robert said. "But the carcass was still lying there. And yet the children swore that they had seen it get up onto its knees, then its feet, shake its head and go off."

They had obviously seen the spirit of the deer leave the body, most children being extremely psychic. I think we can all recall similarly inexplicable things we experienced when we were children, but did not have the ability to realise fully their significance at the time. Something that can be very upsetting to a child is seeing dead animals at the side of roads, whether main routes or country lanes, sacrificial victims of we humans' desire for speed – dogs, cats, foxes, badgers, hedgehogs and birds. This can of course be equally upsetting for adults.

My Druid friend Gavin, who travels round a lot in the course of his work, on seeing such victims always says the following:

(With palms of both hands held down)

Road kill.
Blood spill.

(With palms of both hands held up)

Spirit free –
Blessed be!

If driving, the person's hands should never of course leave the steering wheel. In such situations 'hand' movements are performed mentally. But this kind of prayer can help anyone to feel they are contributing something positive to the natural order of things. Indeed, it would have been nice to think that someone perhaps had said these words at the moment Robert's children saw the spirit of the deceased deer leaving its body.

9
Dark Shadows

Of course there can be a dark side to all sightings, including those of animals. Traditional ghost stories often include many chilling tales of creatures that startle the unwary traveller at night with their large, fiery eyes, something indescribable in their mouths and blood dripping from between their teeth – terrifying Hounds of Hell, the real stuff of legend. So what about the sightings of such beasts?

The most common type of animal that appears in such report is the spectral hound, particularly when described as large and black. The phenomenon of black dog sightings seems to go back far into the mists of time. There are said to be connections with the Hounds of Odin. Generally, most spectral black dogs tend to inhabit deserted areas of countryside, prehistoric tracks, old roadways (not modern ones), ancient ruins and burial mounds. For example, there are tales of Black Shuck, a ghostly dog that roams the Suffolk marshes. An exception perhaps is the urban Barguist, a supposed man-eating black canine with glowing red eyes which reputedly roams the narrow streets of York in search of human prey.

Stephen Wilde, a friend and dowser, told me he believed black dogs were thought forms which were marshalled into existence originally by the Celtic tribal holy men or Druids who took nine years to learn their craft. To become a Master Druid they studied for a total of twenty-seven years. They held in store a wide knowledge of medicines and, he thought, a capacity for the occult – including the bringing into being of thought forms (or tulpas).

"My belief is that these dogs were simply protective devices," he continued. "On a farm near to Leek in Staffordshire there is a burial mound with a protective ring around it that is still very powerful. As far as a dowser is concerned, once you're in, you're in! Legend has it that lions have been seen within the area of the mound, although it is more likely to be the shaggy, large-eyed giant dog, or 'shuk'.

"There are numerous stories concerning these beasts, like the one where a young woman in the 1950s was walking back from a dance at Winsford to her home in Exford, Somerset, late one night. After a while she became aware of some gypsies approaching from the opposite direction. Somewhat the worse for drink, they were pointing at her, laughing, joking and using obscene language! As they drew level she thought they were doing to attack her, but suddenly they withdrew, flattening themselves against the roadside, obviously terrified. Strangely, her feeling of vulnerability was replaced by a sense of great safety and warmth. Immediately she had passed them by, they scattered into the hills. She looked down and there was a great dog walking at her side that came up to her waist."

There have been encounters of all kinds in all sorts of terrifying, lonely places, their weird atmosphere sometimes easy enough I think to pick up even during daylight hours. Some people might dismiss such thoughts as fanciful. That is easy enough to do if you are rushing through the area by car on the way from A to B. But many such areas are powerful enough even to penetrate the metal and glass cocoon in which the average motorist might find himself.

Listening to Stephen reminded me of the story I had heard of where a man, still living in 1900, often recounted the time years before when he was walking through the Aberglaslyn Pass late one night from Porthmadog to his home in Beddgelert. He suddenly noticed that a huge mastiff had appeared at his side. Terrified, he broke into a cold sweat and felt glued to the spot. But before he was able to decide what to do, the dog simply vanished.

Someone by the name of David Evans actually saw the beast twice in the same locality. The second time the mastiff appeared as a fiery vision, scaring not only him but the horse he was riding. Both, it seemed, took several days to recover from the trauma.

I was eager for more intriguing storytelling from Stephen.

"Besides being protective, these dogs can also appear to mark death," he said. "There was someone for instance who worked at a saddlers in Minehead, Devon which, for him, meant an early morning walk into town. On one occasion a large black dog the size of a calf came across a field, traversed the road in front of him and started pawing at the door of a cottage. He didn't think any more about it - except that he'd seen a large black dog – until about 11AM that morning, when someone came in to where he was working and said: 'Hey, Jim! Have you heard old Sam's died?' And the cottage where the black dog had stopped was old Sam's."

It is amazing how one can suddenly stumble upon something that holds on to negativity in all sorts of places – from sheer sadness to downright ghastliness. I think it is almost as though beneath the landscape, in all its varying forms, there runs parallel to it one of blackness, fed on folklore, dark superstition, encompassing the cry in the night, the swirl of a ghostly black cloak, the flash in the moonlight of a spectral dagger, emphasising intense feeling that is still being held there. This need not just be focused on buildings, ancient tracks, ghost lines and witch roads – which can easily be picked up by dowsers and psychics - but on hollows in the ground, even individual trees and rocks.

My Druid friend Gavin told me that while walking through an old churchyard once, he sensed something extremely negative and depressing about one of the large trees there. On making enquiries he discovered that it had in other times been used as a hanging tree. Returning to the churchyard, he put both arms around the trunk and blessed it.

The daughter of another friend was riding her horse at Ipstones, on the Staffordshire Moorlands one day when they happened to approach a particular rock protruding from the ground. She suddenly felt overcome by a strange, negative feeling, and the horse just refused to go past the rock. Later she learned that this had been the location, long ago, for animal sacrifice. Obviously the strong feeling of slaughter, through the pain and suffering involved, was still there just as in places where disasters like fire, flood and plague have occurred the presence of troubled spirits can still be felt, in need of positive redress from the psychic investigator.

Roads, tracks haunted by spirits from way back, as already mentioned, or even more recently through the occurrence of accidents, seem to retain the pall of old griefs, losses and disasters. This may seem relatively obvious or, on the other hand, more subtle by contrast, like some aspects of haunted properties. Places like old workhouses, orphanages and asylums where terrible things, cruelty, torture, and tragic deaths took place over a long time can still convey their petrified atmosphere, whether they are now in ruins or converted into modern business premises. But the hustle and bustle of such positive activity and the daily coming and going of employees can often go some of the way towards healing the negativity of a place.

Initially one might be reluctant to think of visiting sites like former concentration camps, scenes of death and utter degradation on a huge scale. Although we cannot physically go back in time and stop what happened, as in all cases of tragedy we can – and must - always face those dark shadows fairly and squarely; thus making some positive contribution towards *all* places so troubled no matter to what extent. Lighting candles and saying prayers – as so many people do already – helps towards achieving the desired balance.

Inevitably many psychics encounter this dark side in the course of their work. In fact some seem to be specialists in this form, and are called out to what seem to me like some very unique cases. Such cases are not commonly known about, or if they are, can be distorted by the media.

I originally did my interview with Brenda Diskin to include in the chapter on *Tools Of Their* Trade. But when she told me about two of her cases, I felt it more appropriate to follow on here with what she had to say. Like other investigators I have consulted, she is called in by recommendation.

"Before going," she said, "I normally ask for protection from my guides, draw a ring of white light around myself and say prayers of a personal type."

"And what do you take with you?" I asked.

"A white candle and holder," she replied, "with a bowl of salt and another bowl to put water into, then orange-scented smudge-sticks. You have to go in with a very positive state of mind," she continued. "It's no good being upset or nervous. This would definitely cause more upset, as some spirits do pick up negativity from you.

"When dealing with a case I prefer to do so on my own, without the property owner or occupier being there, although I gather as much background as possible from them as back-up, to confirm what I might be up against."

I asked her if she would like to talk about one or two cases, having sensed that perhaps something unusual or even sinister was about to emerge. I was right!

"There was a lady in Hayes, Middlesex who contacted me," she began. "Over a period of time one of her young sons, aged 10, had been pinched and pushed about in bed at night. He also said that he had been 'touched', and had seen the figure of a man in his room. Naturally," continued Brenda, "he became too afraid to go in there, let alone sleep!

"We (my guides and myself) discovered there were two entities in the house. Firstly a man of particularly nasty character. Secondly an unhappy little spirit boy, who would start off clockwork and electric toys on the floor day or night, that belonged to the (living) boys. This spirit even started one off when I walked into the house!"

"Did you think the spirits of the man and the boy were from different times?" I asked her.

"I believe the boy could have been there some time before the man," she responded. "Probably going back to World War Two, whereas the man, I felt, had only been around between five and eight years. He didn't *want* to leave because of the (living) boys in the house. Possibly because he was a paedophile. I had to take more drastic measures – performing certain rites and rituals to dismiss him," she concluded.

At least he passed on I thought, remembering the nasty individual Mel and Amy Howlett had encountered in that flat on the south coast who had refused to pass on, despite all the help that had been offered to him.

Sensing my rapt attention, Brenda proceeded; "A friend of mine who worked for a church in London had experienced 'things' when alone in the building, although other people had experienced them too. It was a very lively little church indeed, psychically, with spirits in there from all sorts of different times.

"I picked up on a little girl from a former building nearby who had been locked up in a room down in the crypt. My friend, having done some research, discovered there had once been a workhouse across the road, a setting for much abuse, cruelty and injustice. Children from there were encouraged to visit the church, but were locked up when they arrived and sold to the colonies. I had found the actual room in the crypt where they were imprisoned, which contained a lot of other spirits as well. The crypt had also been used to store dead bodies from the blitz during World War Two prior to burial. There had also been links with Aleister Crowley. So there was a lot of activity!"

That name seemed familiar to me, somehow. I then recalled Crowley to have been reputedly involved in black magic during the earlier part of the 20th century.

"My guides and I sorted things out for the little girl," Brenda continued, "and for a crippled boy of about fourteen, as well as clearing all the negative influences from the church."

I think we can agree that some buildings obviously appear to be spectacularly haunted and these tend to catch the interest and imagination of many people for a considerable period of time. Such a place, of course, was the infamous Rectory in the village of Borley, in Essex. This had quite a story! Built in 1863 on the site of an old parsonage, it became a mecca for numerous ghosts and weird happenings – including the spirit of a former rector seen on the stairs, a phantom coach and horses seen passing nearby, disembodied voices heard, strange smells experienced, as well as ghostly footsteps, poltergeist activity, objects appearing and disappearing – not to mention the phantom nun which is said to still haunt the area today. This is despite the fact that there is nothing left of the building, since it mysteriously burnt down in 1939. As an intriguing corollary to this strange tale, it was even reported that people saw a number of ghosts looking on while the catastrophe was actually happening. Very weird indeed!

I have been told by more than one psychic, that not always need a place be considered as 'the most haunted' purely because of the number of ghosts that might be present. More likely the term is earned by the intensity, or how badly, the house is haunted. Encounters with ghosts can leave the recipient severely shaken, but sometimes the effect can be even greater. Plas Gwynant, a large house in Nantgwynant, North Wales was reputed to be haunted with various sightings and experiences of 'weird goings-on' over a number of years in the 19th century. But on one occasion a maidservant was found in the grounds in a state of collapse. She managed to reveal only that she had seen 'something terrible' – but some six months later she died apparently as a result of the shock she had sustained. The underlying menace of a badly haunted place can be far more subtle than more spectacular hauntings which can wax and wane.

Initially the house (or presence) may seem to say: "Welcome, welcome!" rather like the sinister Master of Ceremonies in the musical *Cabaret*. "Come in! Look around! Enjoy yourselves!" And to visitors the building may appear to be wonderful, olde worlde and so on. But those who return a number of times – particularly if they are psychic (which most of us are to a greater or lesser extent) – may begin to feel the true nature of that presence as it 'susses out' those it likes and those it dislikes, particularly the very psychic person who is able to 'see' it for what it really is.

The person living there may be of a mind to simply thrive on the house's reputation with a considerable degree of success and with him or her, the presence would feel safe, even protected. By contrast, later occupants could well succumb to the 'darkness' and would either have to get out or be taken over by whatever is present in the house – perhaps to the extent of being driven out of their mind. This can be a very real danger. It's not just a story.

Reading about some spooky situation, listening to the radio, or watching a programme on the television or cinema-screen, however horrific, the comfort factor is that if things get too scary we can shut the book, switch off the radio or television or even quietly tiptoe out of the cinema. Problem solved! In other words we have control over the situation. But supposing we did not possess control, that dark forces actually did manifest themselves in the very place where we lived?

Until some time ago when I seriously began researching for this book, like most 'laymen' my own answer to that scenario would have been to say, "Bring in the exorcist!" I have since learned that is not necessarily the answer, thanks to becoming aware of that marvellous band of investigators who go in quietly, efficiently, sometimes facing vicious spirits, in the hope of offering them empathy and help to enable them to pass on to wider horizons. Investigators like Fabia for example, on the occasion described when she found herself dealing with someone from the German Gestapo, or Brenda Diskin encountering a suspected paedophile.

There are many genuine horrific presences and energies around. But all things considered, the evil and wickedness perceived may not come from the spirits themselves. It is more likely to be the fault of particular individuals when they were here in the land of the living. Because of what they found within themselves many have discovered when it was time to pass on that they were too terrified to do so, and have become trapped by their own fear of whatever reprisals they thought they would have to face. Evil is often what people do to themselves, nothing to do with the world of the spirit. Isolated by their wickedness in life, so in death the ghosts of such people can remain.

It is claimed that all souls are met with great compassion on the other side but that does not excuse them for what they have done. Most flawed souls become flawed not only because of the damage done to them but because of their own choices and actions. They have to be saved eventually, they cannot just be dismissed unless everything offered as help they simply resist. By allowing people freedom of choice, likewise ghosts too, must have that same freedom to accept or not.

In difficult situations within these darker regions, the investigator might find himself trying to put surface plasters over deep, deep wounds. It is like working in the equivalent of an emergency unit. And he himself could end up damaged. That is why many investigators sometimes find it necessary to go through long and elaborate preparations beforehand, in order to protect themselves as best they can. Talking to such people, I realised too that it may take a week or more afterwards for a psychic investigator to recover and to clear the system of negativity. Also that his or her house needs to be cleansed and protected or else the family too could be affected.

Sometimes, I am told, you can pick up not ghosts but terrifying entities from early civilisations, even pre-religious ones from societies that were 'primitive', hugely ancient spirits that are very wicked and evil. Psychics have told me about particular types that originate in ancient Africa which can travel, via people, to occupy property. Atmospheres can be made extremely unpleasant because these entities have been invited in and allowed to flourish on negative forms of thought.

This sort of entity or presence, fortunately, is comparatively rare in the West. "It is different to the more usual sort of thing one is likely to encounter," Dilys said. If it is not recognised, it can be difficult to cope with. Certain types are very much prevalent in the Caribbean, where they originally arrived from Africa via the slave trade. Entities like these can latch on to people causing untold mayhem, malevolence, demonic evil, so much so they can even drive their victim mad if not dealt with. Their equivalent, one could say, would have been the sort of parasitic energies flourishing as a result of superstition, ignorance and fear in medieval England.

"If you are encountering a very evil, malevolent or dark spirit," says Dilys "in all spirit work, it is essential to try to 'know its name'. Despite one's own revulsion, one has to try to allow the light through, however terrible the entity, because dark forces can only be overcome by the light. So you must look the presence in the face – that is a very basic rule to work on and is the only way to tackle the weapons of fear that darkness carries.

"Often you find that with knowledge about the thing you will gain understanding and be able to link in to it with some sense of compassion, of God, or whatever."

There are some people who, disposed towards power, prey on weakness, and are obviously not very positive members of the community. They work with fear and superstition, thus building on negative energy. Delia, a spiritualist medium who has travelled all over the world and describes herself as providing a telephone to the spirits, told me about such a person she met whilst visiting the Caribbean a few years ago.

"She was a lady who practised black magic," Delia said. "She called on spirits who were 'in calamity' – meaning those being stuck between Earth and the Spirit World – to haunt living individuals. She showed me the underside of both her arms, which were covered with massive bruising where these spirits had initially gained their energy from her. Obviously intent on carrying on with her practise, she said that they would eventually kill her, once they had completely drained her of energy."

Often, according to Dilys, when dealing with certain races of people – or individuals retaining old superstitious attitudes - you probably encounter a more tabloid sort of mentality, where they believe you will have to use dramatic stuff like curses and lightning striking to deal with the problem, beliefs that are based on ritual drama. They want to see some action, the bigger the better, and tend not to accept that simply by calling and relying on help from Spirit, prayers and positivity, candles, salt, etc, you can be more effective. They don't understand the subtleties of choice, the ramifications of the balance of positive and negative. To them things are polarised – Good or Evil, Black or White.

No matter where we may travel throughout the world there are still spirits to be encountered, poised somewhere in that limbo between here and the Spirit World, for different reasons.

During a visit to Barbados Geraldine Edmonds, a working medium, remembered picking up the spirit of a doctor who had been concerned with eye problems among the slaves. Appearing to her through a spiritual rainbow, he told her he did not want to leave the island, preferring to remain near the old sugar plantations. Personally, on hearing this story, I wondered if the reason for his lingering was that maybe he did not realise he had died.

Delia recalled visiting a National Interest house whilst holidaying in the Caribbean.

"During the guided tour I noticed a native Indian lady (a spirit lady) sitting in a corner of one of the rooms," she told me. "When I made contact with her, she told me she was trapped by something evil and couldn't cross over to the next world. At the end of the tour I asked the owners if I could return to the room, and they agreed.

"The spirit told me she was an Arawak Indian, a member of the original people on the island. She had been there since the 17th century and was one of the indentured slaves to a white master, who kept making her pregnant but drowned her children in a pond. He was still there in spirit, and would not let her pass on. She asked me to help her, and to find her children.

"I saw him – a big, tall man in a cap, with a small scar on his face - as the room went very cold. He tried to scare me but I linked in with my loved ones, who have always protected me, as I attempted to push him into a far corner of the room. And they came and took him away. There was suddenly a white light, like a porthole, and all her seven children came to meet the Indian lady and took her to the light.

"When I spoke to the owner, he told me he had seen the Indian lady from time to time. She, with the other Indians, would have been kept at the back of the premises with the Irish (indentured) slaves. He also told me the house had been built over the pond where the drownings had occurred, and said he had never had a good night's sleep. But afterwards, the house felt at peace.

"On returning to England I was given confirmation by another medium who asked if I knew someone named 'Melissa', an Indian lady. The spirit had obviously come back to say thanks."

I was conducting this interview with Delia on the phone, and at this point there was a long silence. In fact she thought we had been cut off. Not so, it was just that I felt so aghast at the horrific and callous cruelty involved in the story. She went on to tell me of another occasion when she had a similar encounter with a bullying spirit that was too scared to move on, again when she was on holiday in the Caribbean.

"Rose Hall was owned by a wicked Irish woman named Annie Palmer in the 17th century. She used to beat her black slaves and hang them for her own pleasure. Touring through the house, a group of us – including three other psychics besides myself – were conducted into her bedroom. The room temperature dropped rapidly, and what looked like an indentation appeared on Annie's bed where she would have lain. Seeing this strange manifestation, a lot of our group, who were West Indian, panicked and ran out of the room.

"But we psychics stayed, so she confronted us with such cold it was as if our feet were in quicksand. We linked in all of us to Spirit. Again, there was a great white light around. The next thing I knew was that the room became very bright – and she went. A few minutes later, we looked out of the window, and saw a tall black man in ragged clothes. We were able to identify him as her 'free' slave (her overseer), called Itomie. Like Melissa in the other story, he too must have come back to thank us that he, and no doubt many others, had been able to move on to the Light."

This I found another incredibly horrific and cruel part in the history of the area. But I was amazed at the conclusion!

"When we got home," Delia said, "we had photographs developed, some of which we'd taken inside Rose Hall. On one, where a friend's face should have been, there was Annie's face staring from out of a mirror!"

Being aware of the general sweep of history, as most of us are, usually brings to mind overall thoughts about ambition, power, lust and self-gratification. But it is only when we consider the examples like the ones just quoted, of sadistic injustice and cruelty meted out to the individual that their plight is fully realised as well as the 'sickness' of those who administer such treatment – something which is not recorded in all the history books. Many such cases, alas, still unwritten, get handed on by word of mouth.

What the experts say

My experts have probably made comments on most aspects of the subject of this chapter by now, but Geraldine Edmonds told me the following story.

"A few years ago I had just moved into a house and this particular night, lying on a futon, I woke up feeling a tremendous pressure on my chest. At the same time I could hear a loud rattling of chains and saw this horrible Alsatian dog. Then I heard a woman's voice, sounding like that of an old crone, saying: "I want to go through you, Elsie!" Needless to say, it was scary. But summoning all my strength I told the entity, in no uncertain terms to f...k off! And it did!

"Later, as I got to know the neighbours, it turned out a couple of elderly spinster sisters had lived in the house opposite. A short time back, one of them had died. The surviving sister was named Elsie.

"I keep various crystals around the house," Geraldine told me "to encourage the positive energies. I did have an obsidian (a black stone), which is concerned with past lives, but I found it too negative and oppressive. Whenever I tuned in I would make contact with a black angel, so eventually I got rid of it.

Geraldine has 'seen' things since she was a child. "I remember particularly seeing what appeared like a mother and child who both seemed extremely thin – so much so I could see right through them. I called them the 'Polythene People'. It was very odd and quite frightening."

Simon's comment when I asked him about the 'dark side' was that there are any number of reasons why people react to spirits, and why spirits react to people.

"Not every haunting is a cry for help," he said. "It could be energy being in the wrong place, rather than it being 'bad' as such. Saying it is a bad force could cause it to take advantage of this. All the spirit might be doing is trying to defend or assert itself.

"For me, it's a matter of being firm, very firm, saying: 'Go back to the Light, where you originally came from!'

"There's always the danger of feeding them, or even harming the ghosts that need help."

Dilys comments: "When you ever encounter the 'dark side' you have to stand your ground as both Geraldine and Simon have illustrated, and try to be firm and act with authority. But the authority comes from what you represent – a source of enlightenment, not any power of your own. In the end, it's not up to you to pass judgements."

10

A Disappearing Act

Do ghosts run their course and then fade away? This is a question that has intrigued people for a long time. But there are many instances where they have disappeared other than by being 'released' or sent on their way with the help of a medium or investigator. This might be for any number of reasons. For instance they could have felt ignored, or that the reason for their presence was no longer relevant. This can occur over a long period where sightings can become less frequent, gradually becoming paler until only their presence can be felt – then finally, nothing. Or the disappearance can be relatively swift, when a building is altered, say, or even demolished. Ghosts or spirits do not always make a habit of lingering once former haunts have gone. The next property built on such a site could well prove to be quite spirit-free.

An interesting case I came across regarding some of these aspects told of an old house (location not given) in which, during the 18th century, the figure of a woman was often seen in a red dress, red shoes and complete with black head-dress. Sixty or so years later, her apparel had faded to pink. By 1850 people who saw her ghost reported that she appeared to be dressed in white, and her hair had turned to grey. Prior to World War Two her presence was indicated only by ghostly footsteps and the swish of her long dress. But it was in the early 1970s that workmen finally moved in to demolish the old house. They said that although they had neither seen nor heard anything, they had definitely sensed a presence there. But nothing, so I understand, has been reported since.

In his very comprehensive book *Ghost World*, first published in 1893, the author T.F. Thiselton Dyer quoted an example of another bored(?) lady spirit who haunted Astwood Court, once the seat of the Culpeper family. An old oak table removed from against the side-panelling in a particular room in 1816 was found to bear the impression of her fingers. It was suggested at the time that, tired of appearing for no particular reason, she had vented her anger at the table and then disappeared for ever. Personally, I couldn't blame her!

The Llindir Inn at Henllan near Denbigh, North Wales, said to have been built in 1229, still retains its thatched roof and rough stone walls. It was said to be haunted by the ghost of a lady who had been strangled by her jealous husband, a previous landlord of the old hostelry. Her ghost used to be seen in her bedroom, but one guest claimed she actually attacked him and pushed him downstairs while other guests who had slept in the same room reported being pushed out of bed, or grabbed by the throat. In 1974 however, in a letter to the magazine *Country Quest* a reader came up with the information that the Llindir ghost had not made herself manifest for some time, so it was assumed she had been upset by modernisation having been carried out at the premises and had left.

As discussed earlier in the book, assuming that a moment of high emotion, positive or otherwise is somehow preserved in the ground, the atmosphere or the fabric of a building to be re-enacted at certain times, this requires the release of energy thus stored. It is similar perhaps to a battery – which as we all know, if not recharged will eventually run out of electrical energy. So too with ghosts or spirits maybe. Many events such as old battles being seen re-enacted in the sky over the battlegrounds where they were actually fought are seen no more, apart from certain paranormal bits of peripheral activity. Even the energy levels sustaining high feelings and emotions tend to drop eventually. And yet some energy levels seem to last a lot longer than others. There are many people who claim to have seen the ghosts of Roman soldiers until quite recently, but much nearer to our own time the Battle of Naseby, for example, fought near Market Harborough Northamptonshire in 1645 during the Civil War and seen in spectral replay in the sky for a long time afterwards, has had no repeat performances for many, many years.

I am not aware of reports of any ghostly sightings that could pre-date those of Roman soldiers. And there seem to be no visible spirits of cavemen, prehistoric animals, or even any as recent as mammoths or sabre-toothed tigers. Bearing in mind that some ghosts of Roman soldiers have been seen 'from the knees up', because the road or ground levels are higher now, it might not be too fanciful to suggest that there could still be energy levels sufficient to sustain ghosts of prehistoric animals which continue to roam areas of the world now completely submerged by natural earth movement and sea incursion. Remember that the spirit world seems to have dimensions so different to our own. Perhaps Jules Verne's *Journey To The Centre Of The Earth* may be nearer to the truth than we realise!

Sometimes there is the more interactive kind of ghost that will manifest itself perhaps just once. Like that of a person who shortly after death appears to a friend or relative – not always just to bid them a fond farewell, but in the hope of resolving unfinished business. An elderly lady told me that not long after he died, her father had appeared to her future brother-in-law. During the latter part of his life the older man, to his displeasure and embarassment, had worn leg-irons which had been put into the garden shed after his death. This had not met with the spirit's approval and he told the young man he wanted them buried in the garden, and forgotten about. The deed was thus carried out, and her father's spirit, according to the elderly lady, must have been happy as a result because it was never seen again.

Another lady in her late twenties related a fascinating incident to me that happened when she was about 12 years of age. In her own words:

"My grandma lived on the Wirral, Cheshire and I used to go with my parents at weekends to visit her. It had been a really hot summer and this particular Saturday evening we were returning home to Leek, in Staffordshire. We were somewhere between Frodsham and Delamere when I suddenly felt compelled to say to my mother that someone had died. She told me not to be so silly. Although it was a very warm evening, going dusk with the car side-windows open, I was absolutely shivery and frozen. Again I told Mum I could feel that someone had died and again she told me to shut up!

"We were coming through a forest I remember, along a straight road and I saw a white Mini and a person inside. I started to scream and was clutching my throat. Because I was hysterical, my mother stopped the car, came round and smacked me. And where the white Mini had been, it had vanished except for glass on the road where we had stopped. My mother hadn't even seen the Mini!

"Five days later we heard from my aunt who lived in the area. She said that earlier on that particular Saturday there had been a head-on collision at the same point, some hours before the time I had 'seen' the white Mini. A young girl in an actual white Mini had died – her neck had been broken. I felt it and saw it so vividly. I felt so connected with it."

Unlike the previous case where the individual was approached by a spirit, this was an occasion when someone had obviously picked up and inter-related with a tragedy by chance while actually passing through a particular area. To my knowledge she did not experience it again when in the same vicinity, but it would be interesting to find out if that particular white Mini and its hapless passenger have been seen by anyone else since.

It was during a very enjoyable day out in the Derbyshire Peaks that I encountered Christine, a pleasant, mild-mannered woman in her mid-fifties and heard from her the following two stories in which she had felt very much involved.

About thirty years ago she and some relatives over from Australia had been walking down a country lane in Nottinghamshire when they came across an elderly man dressed in slightly old-fashioned clothes, leaning against a five-bar gate by a field. They stopped and talked with him for some time.

"We don't have the coaches down here like we used to do," was one of his remarks.

The lane being very narrow, Christine and her relatives thought privately that coaches would never have been able to get along the track at all but thought no more of it. Before going on their way the old character posed with them for a photograph. When the film was developed however, they noticed that where he should have been standing there was a gap, with only part of the five-bar gate showing instead. It was then that the idea came to them that maybe, considering his old-fashioned attire, he had been referring to horse-drawn coaches of a time far longer past than they had assumed. But he had appeared to them as solid as themselves.

Although no photograph was in evidence I felt the true conviction in Christine's telling of the story, and although at the time she and her relatives did not realise they were dealing with a ghost, there are similar stories where photographs have been taken of the paranormal though few of them in my opinion have really been proved to be genuine.

"Several years ago I bought an original painting from an artist in Nottingham," Christine continued, "depicting a hump-backed stone bridge going over a canal at Whatstandwell, a rural area between Cromford and Ambergate in Derbyshire, close to where we live. I decided it would make a nice present for my sister and her husband because there were sentimental associations. For several years prior to her death, it had been a routine of our mother, when going for a walk, to pause in the middle of that bridge and gaze down into the water.

"Within a couple of weeks of my sister and her husband receiving the painting, my sister rang to say that there was a figure of a woman in a red coat on the bridge in the picture. 'It's Mum!' she said, flabbergasted.

"I thought she was joking – until I saw for myself.

"It was absolutely amazing and 'Mum' seemed to remain in the picture for several weeks, before she slowly faded away. I enquired of the artist whether he had painted the picture over something else. The answer was that he hadn't. The canvas had been brand new."

It seemed very strange that Christine's mother seemed to 'arrive' suddenly in the picture and stay there for a while before finally fading. But there have been numerous examples of photographs and paintings of people who have passed on that have faded, not over years necessarily but sometimes in a matter of weeks or months. In *Psychic News*, it was recently reported that a tapestry on board the liner QE2 depicting the late Princess Margaret had suffered a similar fate, her features having faded as her health deteriorated during the months before her death.

Earlier I mentioned how a few years ago I came to take over the large, neglected garden of a house just south of the Staffordshire Potteries and how I was apparently watched over by 'Mr X', the previous owner of the property who had died five years earlier. As I have said, the general atmosphere of the place was warm and positive, as though there had been a lot of happiness in the past. And as progress continued over the next couple of years at pulling back the grounds to their previous magnificence, 'Mr X' continued to show great interest, appearing on the terrace and then vanishing quite frequently.

Maintenance had to take over more from restoration or else the whole would have returned to wilderness, but a day came in summer when the task was completed. I pushed the final barrow-load of brash through the narrow gateway at the bottom of the garden to the bonfire down in the old orchard.

Something made me look up at the house, which was quite close, and at the top of some steps at the back of the car-port, 'Mr X' was standing. Within the earthly, familiar time-span it seemed he disappeared immediately, while in another in which I suddenly found myself – and I had not previously experienced – it seemed we were cautiously considering each other for a very long period like lions meeting for the first time. Then I sensed warmth emanating from his soft blue eyes. As I found myself smiling, he reacted with a slow nod of approval and then was gone. I was to remain for another three years caring for the garden, but I never saw 'Mr X' again after that day.

A recent TV programme about the Sutton Hoo discoveries detailed how archaeologists were directed by spirit guidance to dig for 'buried treasure' and Dilys encountered a similar story when she first started her career in journalism. She did a lot of research into Welsh folklore and came across the tale of a place near to Mold, North Wales called Bryn yr Elillion which means 'Hill of the Elves and Fairies'. Apparently, according to local tradition it had been haunted by something described as a 'golden ghost' and when eventually excavated by archaeologists, it was found to be a burial mound of some ancient personage of importance. Various artefacts were found including a very valuable necklace called a torque, which was made of gold and is now housed in a museum.

In recent years a lot of building has taken place in the area and there seem to be no more reports of the 'golden ghost' having been seen. After the mound was excavated, perhaps the ghost felt that the need for guard duty was over. But might the presence of a supernatural phenomenon actually have drawn attention to the fact that something desirable was buried there, as opposed to the ghost having been 'invented' to deter anyone from robbing the grave? This was said to be ancient tradition yet who knows, perhaps it could have been some Victorian archaeologists who had said they saw a ghost that started off the whole paranormal connection to the site in the first place.

On a bright winter's day Dilys and I decided to get out and about to check on whether ghosts are still around in likely places such as Eyam, in the Derbyshire Peak District. This was the village that achieved fame when it isolated itself from the surrounding area in order to contain an outbreak of bubonic plague in 1664-5. More than 300 of its inhabitants fell victim to an appalling kind of death as a result. We felt that while things were quiet prior to the forthcoming tourist season, this might be the best time to pick up on atmosphere or sense any presences that might have lingered.

Personally I got the impression it was tourism that haunted the village, rather than spiritual links to the 17th century. I was astounded, considering this to be the site *en masse* of so much courage, fear, suffering and death. Had all the ghosts gone away? Or had they simply moved on to greater horizons, having achieved peace at last? Perhaps it was the faith the villagers had – albeit having been tested to the fore – and their supreme courage that enabled this to happen.

I wondered, because to my eyes Eyam appeared to be so well-planned, a model village, like an outdoor film set. There was just one place – the shell of a cottage I noticed, with trees growing through the roof – that could have given space to a presence, tucked neatly away behind two very much-lived-in cottages along the Foolow Road.

The spirit of Catharine Mompesson, wife of the Rector Charles Mompesson, who died during the terrible epidemic is claimed to have appeared frequently in the churchyard of St. Lawrence's where she is buried. She and her husband did much to help the victims and their families before she herself became a victim.

This is what Dilys reported.

'I had no sense of disaster. If I had not been told this was the Plague Village, I would not have known. I didn't go into any of the cottages, but I got a strong sense of the past. But which past? I felt a domineering, autocratic presence here in the form of a person, or persons, which gave me the impression it had been a place where people did as they were told, possibly emanating from a religious type of regime but from which era I don't know. I felt that the people had very little freedom of thought and private life. Possibly, this was due to some form of Puritanism. Whether this was anything to do with the plague or not, again I don't know.'

The origins of Eyam go far back to Celtic times, with a fine stone cross in the churchyard dating from the period, which represented a point of worship prior to the Norman Invasion. And yet by contrast, throughout the history of the Industrial Revolution, entire communities were likely to be created almost overnight. Although times and conditions were hard, people related in such places, not only to their work but to each other over several generations, as they had done over a much wider time scale in more ancient settlements like Eyam. Cameraderie, competition and concern for others flourished. But whenever economic climates have changed, many such communities have been destroyed with little or nothing remaining. Except their ghosts, perhaps? Or, realising there is no point in hanging around, have they moved on also? Maybe not. A community that lasted for only a hundred years could well prove to have more ghosts than one similar that survived ten times longer.

One such place was where Dilys grew up.

"My village was built in the mid 1800s more or less from scratch, to house people who worked at the local iron works," she told me. "Called the Lodge, it was situated about three miles from Wrexham, North Wales. It was built in a dip between two hills in a country area that was considered to be so isolated that it was said the fairies danced there.

"A hundred years or so later (in the early 1970s), the steel company bought up the entire village – every building, every scrap of land - in a programme of expansion. Every inch was razed to the ground for use as car parks and for opencast mining. Since then the works have closed and the whole area has been left wild and weed-infested. When I went back on a visit, I was driven up the original road that just stopped at nothing but trees and undergrowth. I couldn't recognise any features of the landscape. It was as though the village had never been.

"I remember living there for nineteen years. It was a teeming place, so full of life, with chapels, shops and houses. I feel it was very much like the village in *Under Milk Wood*, filled with all sorts of characters. On my visit it was evening, and very quiet. Being psychic, I could still 'hear', 'feel' and 'see' the village just out of physical sight through the trees. It was very unsettling. Sad for me, wondering where my childhood home had once stood. Even sadder to feel the life still there, but gone.

"I could well imagine that people who knew nothing of the village would go down that road and find themselves sensing or even 'seeing' something. I wondered if any of us who had lived there were still there, as we used to be. I wondered if I would meet myself as a child on the road. I felt like someone might perhaps have felt in the cases you have recorded where they found they were watching a battle re-enacted. It must have been the same for them afterwards when they 'saw' themselves as phantoms, even though for me it was nineteen years of my growing up. But for the others - the people seeing the battle – it would only be a matter of a couple of hours."

"What effect do you think it could have had," I asked her "if you *had* actually met yourself or any of the villagers you knew on the road?"

"Probably it would have been the most fantastic psychic experience I'd ever have had!" she said quietly after some thought.

Just as the once common sparrows, song-thrushes, larks, frogs, newts and many other species of our gardens and countryside have for environmental reasons dwindled in numbers over the past few years, so too, claims the Society of Psychical Research, have sightings of ghosts or spirits. Numerous reasons have been put forward to try and explain this.

Considering that the spirit world appears to have its own dimensions and rules, functioning on its own frequencies and wavelengths, a recent conjecture is that the increase in the use of mobile phones over the last ten or more years could have had a significant effect on the decline of certain types of paranormal activity. Intensified microwave radiation and electromagnetic fields attributed to the use of these phones seems to have interfered with the sighting and/or audibility of ghosts, a phenomenon that had not hitherto existed over the centuries.

It has been suggested that the use of mobile phones using a slightly different frequency might be introduced. But like many other matters regarding the environment alas, the implementation of ideas contrary to the mainstream of thought takes a long time – and to see some end result even longer.

In a recent issue of *Psychology Today* it was reported that in America, it has been demonstrated that sensitive temporal lobes - the areas of the brain that regulate emotional and motivated behaviour – may be the reason why certain individuals are subject to ghostly encounters. Such individuals are prone, so the article states, to the influence of weak electromagnetic fields such as those man-made, even those created by an electric (mains or battery-driven) bedside clock! Certainly a new idea, though science is continually finding explanations for all kinds of phenomena. But it does make one wonder why ghosts were seen long before such man-made technology came into existence!

Even if modern technology is making a difference to the spirit world, the general feeling is that the majority of ghosts are in the wrong dimension anyway; they should be in the spirit realm, laid to rest and at peace. Yet it is due to this same technology that in hospitals people's lives are being suspended 'in limbo' instead of their being allowed to depart peacefully at their appointed time. In the future, who knows, people may be 'frozen', in order to survive long flights into space. Perhaps from within such realms as these will emerge the ghosts of times to come.

But certainly, according to the people I interviewed for this book, in spite of all such prophesy, there are still ghosts a-plenty about, and still being seen.

The hope of all religions is that the person achieves peace after death. And despite the fact that many spooky stories are set in the churchyard, when sitting in the one at St. Edward's, Leek, in Staffordshire where I used to live, I always picked up a great sense of well being there, of nature and of peace. I think this is common to most churchyards. They are in fact some of the most peaceful of places on earth.